MOTHER AND SON

MOTHER AND SON

by

I. COMPTON-BURNETT

JULIAN MESSNER, INC.

NEW YORK

MGE

Published by Julian Messner, Inc.
8 West 40th Street, New York 18

Copyright 1955, by I. Compton-Burnett

Library of Congress Catalog Card No. 55-7262

CHAPTER I

"The person has arrived, ma'am."

"What person?" said Mrs. Hume.

"The person who was expected, ma'am."

"And who was expecting her?"

"I supposed it was yourself, ma'am. It would be the assumption."

"And how would you refer to someone I was expecting?"

"I understood she was to be under consideration, ma'am."

"Is that an answer to my question?"

"The lady has arrived, ma'am. She has found her way," said the parlourmaid, with a change in her tone.

"Found her way? What do you mean?"

"Along that road from the station, ma'am. Under the shadow of all those trees. The dusk is already threatening."

"You can show her in," said Miranda Hume, not raising her eyes or her hands from the newspaper on her knees. "And you children keep to your side of the room and appear to be occupied. You can stay where you are, my son."

Two boys and a girl exchanged a glance and moved away, and were actually occupied in giving their attention to the scene. A middle-aged man remained, as directed, in his seat.

The maid ushered in a neatly dressed woman, who

had an appearance of keeping her personality neutral, in case any particular form should be required.

Miranda had no such aspect. Her tall, upright frame, strong, white hair, firm, unremarkable features and small, pale, experienced eyes gave the impression of being what they were and had reason to be.

"Good-morning, Miss—Burke," she said, referring openly to a paper at her hand, and not concerned with the fact that it was afternoon. "It is good of you to come to see an old woman and to think of being her companion. Will you tell me in what ways you are suited to such a post?"

"I am companionable," said Miss Burke, hesitating in spite of the appositeness of her claim. "And I am interested in other people and their lives."

Miranda's face showed that something confirmed her expectations.

"What is your age?"

"I beg your pardon, Mrs. Hume?"

"How old are you? How many years have you lived?"

"I am over thirty, Mrs. Hume."

"Yes, so I see. So am I. By how much are you over it?"

"I did not expect to be asked my age."

"I am under no obligation to consider that."

"I am not much under forty," said Miss Burke, changing her tone under Miranda's eye. "I am actually forty-seven."

"You would pass for less. You could say you were forty-two. It comes of the easy life of a companion."

"I never tell untruths," said Miss Burke, her answer seeming to cover the whole of Miranda's speech.

"You can give a wrong impression. You do not mind doing that. It would be your object."

"It is a disadvantage to be too old, when you are placed as I am."

"Yes, of course it is," said Miranda, not without sympathy. "But that makes it more important that the falsehood should be plausible."

"I should not use the word, 'falsehood'," said Miss Burke, not mentioning the term of her choice.

"What word would you use?"

Miss Burke still did not give it.

"We will not pursue the matter. Indeed I see we cannot. Are you good-tempered in ordinary life?"

"Yes, I think I am. Of course I have my own opinions."

"Does that mean you would hold to them argumentatively?"

"We cannot alter what we think," said Miss Burke, not without a touch of this quality.

"Surely we can, if light is thrown on a subject. Do you not try to profit by your employer's companionship?"

"It is my companionship that is the point," said Miss Burke, causing herself to smile.

"Do you often change your posts?"

"Never, unless there is some reason."

"Well, I suppose not. Dismissal or your own dissatisfaction. I asked if it was often."

"Not oftener than is natural."

"You regard that as an answer?" said Miranda, sending her eyes over Miss Burke's face, as though receiving light on her.

"I have stayed for some time in some cases, and not in others. I suppose that it is how it must be."

"How it has been with you. So sometimes people do not take to you?"

"Well, sometimes I do not take to them," said Miss Burke, with some spirit.

Miranda nodded to herself, her eyes still on Miss Burke's face.

"Do you for example take to me?"

"It is difficult to judge on a first impression."

"Be quiet, boys," said Miranda, turning and speaking with a hiss in her tone, as there was a sound of mirth. "I think I do not find it so. You would come to me and leave me at your own convenience?"

"Well, you would dismiss me at yours," said Miss Burke, trying to speak lightly.

"Why did you leave your last situation?" said Miranda, with a note of ruthlessness on the last word.

"I found that things were expected of me, that were not in the arrangement."

"You mean you were asked to be useful in the house?" said Miranda, raising her eyes.

"Well, housework has nothing to do with companionship."

"Surely it has, in a case of emergency. If a companion could not rise to that, she would not deserve the name. What did they ask you to do?"

"I need hardly tell you that, Mrs. Hume."

"You will tell me what I wish to know," said Miranda, not disguising the range of her own requirements. "Was it something you cannot mention?"

"They asked me to wash up dishes at the sink," said Miss Burke, in a full tone, as though this idea of Miranda's were not hers.

"Well, where would you wash them? They would not ask you to do so at the piano."

"No, they would not," said Miss Burke, agreeing that this amelioration was not possible.

"What did you say to them?" said Miranda, with the hint of a smile.

"I pointed out that it was not in the arrangement."

"If an emergency arose here, would you expect me to wash the dishes?"

"No," said Miss Burke, on an uncertain note, as though feeling that their attitude to the activity had something in common.

"Then would you leave them unwashed?"

"I would help you to wash them," said Miss Burke, perhaps meaning to strike a companionable note, but doing so too completely.

"Have you a good voice for reading aloud?" said Miranda, in a colder tone.

"It would hardly be different from my ordinary voice."

"Would you read as if you had written the books yourself, and felt self-conscious about them?"

"No, I should only try to interpret them."

"You cannot just read simply and clearly what is before your eyes?" said Miranda, giving a sigh.

"Yes, if that is what you want."

"Well, it naturally is. Why should I wish for your implied opinion? I could ask you for it."

"Well, I would remember that."

"And you would not sit as if you had a host of unspoken thoughts seething within you?"

"It is not likely I should have a host of them."

"Or as if your mind were a blank?"

"I would try to strike the mean."

"I have no liking for smart answers."

"You do not seem to have any liking for answers at all," said Miss Burke, lightening her tone too late.

"Well, I must not waste your time," said Miranda, in an almost pleasant manner. "It is never a kindness to do that. I will give you your fare and meet any other expenses. It was natural to apply for the post; indeed it shows your sense, as it is a good one. I hope you will find another equal to it."

"You do not think we should suit each other, Mrs. Hume?"

"I do not think you would suit me," said Miranda, answering something in the tone. "Our interpretation of companionship is different."

"Have you ever had a companion before?"

"What makes you think I have not?"

"You seem to expect the impossible."

"It is what in a sense I do expect, and feel I cannot face," said Miranda, half to herself. "You will find some tea ready for you in the next room. And this will cover your outlay and give you something over for your time."

"I do not ask anything but my bare expenses, Mrs. Hume."

"But you are glad to have something," said Miranda, handing her an envelope and waiting for her fingers to close on it. "We need not pretend that things are not as they are. I am not a person who does that."

The truth of this caused another sound of mirth, and Miranda sent a rapid frown in its direction. "I hope you will soon find a suitable position. There are many in which you might be useful; that is, if you do not set your face against being so. The maid who gives you tea will tell you about your trains."

Miranda offered her hand without raising her eyes, as though to save herself from seeing the effects of the interview. There was nothing about them to disturb her. Miss Burke went to the door with an air of having dealt as she could with another item on her list.

Someone was there before her. The middle-aged man stood ready to open it, and did so with a bowing movement and a faintly grieved expression. As he closed it, he drew himself up and turned to the room.

"A ship that passes in the night," he said, in deep, almost emotional tones.

"Well, it was better for it to do so quickly. And you need not stand and look after it. It will come to anchor in time."

"I trust we can rely on it, Mother. I trust that it is the view of the stranger within our gates. There is something troubling in the thought of a woman dealing with such difficulties alone. I admit that my thoughts are following the little, lonely figure, as it wends its way along the road to the station."

"It is in the library at the moment. And it is neither lonely nor little. It is of ordinary size and Bates is with it. I heard her go in."

"Your ears are sharper than mine, Mother; I heard nothing."

"I am alive to all that happens in my house."

"And the house is not blind to anything that befalls you, Mother," said Rosebery, with deliberate mirth.

"Well, a house must have a head."

"What a pity, when everyone has to live in a house!" said the girl to her brothers.

"And a sad place it would be without one, Mother," said Rosebery at the same moment.

"What would it be like then?" said the younger boy.

"Someone would become the head," said his sister. "It is a natural law."

"It is time for your tea, Aunt Miranda," said the elder boy. "Is Bates's attention fully occupied?"

"You may ring the bell. No, not you, my son; it is for the boys to do it. They are not here to be looked at and waited on. We have no butler now. Someone has written for Wilson's character. So he will not return."

"What will you say of him?" said Alice.

"His time here constitutes a character. It is of no good to say anything."

"Aunt Miranda's tone has a baffled note," said Francis.

"Have you engaged another?" said Adrian.

"No, I have not. A butler is not a necessity. You had better get those ideas out of your head."

"Who will do his work?" said Alice.

"Bates. She is equal to it. And she can get another woman. Oh, Bates; I am not replacing Wilson; I am not fit for the change. I am giving you his place. It will mean a rise in wages. What do you say to it?"

"I might be willing to oblige you, ma'am," Bates said.

"There is no question of that. The gain would be yours."

"Well, if it is for your convenience, ma'am, I could give it a trial."

"It is 'yes' or 'no'," said Miranda.

"Well, it may as well be in the affirmative, ma'am."

"Is Miss Burke still with you?"

"She has not yet gone out into the dark, ma'am. Someone met his end on that road last week."

"Yes, through a runaway horse. That would not happen again."

"Many things can happen, ma'am. It is not always given to foresee them."

"Well, she is used to looking after herself."

"I would not go alone along that road at night."

"Well, you are not so used to it. You are too well looked after here."

"It is my lot to look after other people, ma'am. And I have not murmured."

"You have very little to murmur about."

"I implied that I was inured, ma'am."

"How do you come home from your chapel on

Sunday nights?" said Miranda, her tone not exalting this manner of worship.

"Someone comes forward, ma'am. There is no lack of what is due. Shall I tell the housemaid to bring the tea? The lady is still under our roof."

"And so entitled to your attendance?"

"It is one of the unspoken words, ma'am."

"But Aunt Miranda spoke it," said Alice.

Miranda frowned at her niece and beckoned her husband from the window. He came across the room, a vigorous man of sixty-eight, with high, hard features, pallid face and hair and hands, and deep, narrow eyes that carried an easy cynicism. He looked with equality at his wife, with acceptance at his son, and with a guarded feeling at his orphan niece and nephews. The latter were like him and like each other, with darker hair and eyes than his, and a livelier aspect. They seemed to welcome his approach and to be easier for his presence.

Julius Hume's eyes rested more seldom on his son. Rosebery's large, heavy frame, full, heavy face and hands, rather elementary features and weak, emotional eyes aroused no pride in his father; and the latter's instinctive feeling for him was tinged with discomfort and pity. Rosebery saw his father as a weightier being than himself, and accepted his dubious affection. He felt no jealousy of him, having no desire for his qualities.

"Why did you not want Miss Bark as a companion, Aunt Miranda?" said Francis.

"It is Miss Burke, as you know. And you know the answer to your question."

"So he does," said Alice. "That is why he wants to hear you give it."

"She would strike the wrong note, and she would not be alive to our atmosphere. And she has the wrong sort of outlook. That is a thing I could not bear."

"No one is perfect," said Adrian.

"Now why feel you must say that? Should I think anyone was? What ground have I for thinking so?"

"It would not become us, Mother, to give any reasons," said Rosebery, leaning forward with a smile.

"Would the right person wish to come," said Julius. "What would be her object?"

"That she would want a life of ease in return for nominal services. The post of companion does not deserve its name. Fewer people would want it, if it did."

"Just as many people would be obliged to have it. And you refused to guarantee that the services would be nominal."

"I would rather give real services than nominal ones," said Alice.

"No, you would not," said her aunt. "You would do anything rather than that. Or you would be a more unusual person than you are."

"Now why should people have this aversion to manual employment?" said Rosebery, looking round. "I have often asked myself the question, and been at a loss for the answer."

"I will give it to you," said his father. "It is because it is seen as requiring a lower intelligence, and because it does require it. And because it is dull and unrewarding in itself."

"I would do anything rather than adapt myself to a single human being," said Francis.

"Adapting oneself to human beings is the essence of usefulness," said his aunt. "And you will have to be useful to earn your bread. There will be no money apart from a little for your sister. We have nothing except what comes from the place, and goes back into it."

"That may not put it so far from Francis," said Julius. "He comes into things after Rosebery."

"And I am so likely to be a bachelor, Father, indeed am so far established in that character, that it is natural to nominate my successor. And I welcome my cousin as heir presumptive, and after him his brother. And I think we may say that our line is secure."

"You may marry at any time and have a son," said Francis. "You are not the type of man that is indifferent to women."

"Rather would I say, Francis, that I am too little indifferent to them," said Rosebery, smiling and then altering his tone. "I think almost any woman could find her way to my heart, indeed would find it open to her; and that might not be the safest road towards matrimony. And talking about my type, I belong to the one that is faithful to the one woman, and that the one who fills the earliest memories." He smiled at his mother.

"So it is Adrian who will face the stress of things," said Alice. "And he is not the most fitted for it."

"I suggest that he should prepare himself for the secondary duties, that I now discharge for my father;

and that he should moreover perform them with more success than his cousin."

"He might do something less suitable," said Julius.

"We cannot plan our lives on the basis of Rosebery's remaining a bachelor," said Francis. "He might marry after Aunt Miranda's death. He would find his life lonely without her."

"You need not concern yourself with his future," said Miranda, her tone perhaps sharper for the allusion to her own.

"Francis, I must deprecate the voicing of that thought," said Rosebery, in troubled remonstrance. "It is enough that I carry it with me. I should undoubtedly—perhaps I should say 'shall'—find my life lonely without her; but it would not in my case constitute a reason for marrying. Rather should I walk with my loneliness as a companion."

"I would rather have ordinary work," said Adrian. "I could not be assistant to Francis. I should always know he was my brother."

"I should feel the same about a cousin," said Francis. "We should be too much on a level."

"Your cousin is not on your level," said Miranda. "He is thirty years older than you, and a weightier personality."

"A weightier person perhaps we should say, Mother," said Rosebery, with his slow laugh. "That will not be disputed."

"The boys can do boys' work for the present," said Julius. "And it is not the easiest kind."

"And work of any kind is a privilege," said

Rosebery. "I often regret that I am in a measure denied it."

"You could do more, if you would," said his father. "I thought it was your object to escape it."

"I need his companionship until my own companion comes," said Miranda. "I am doing my best to get her. I cannot help the low quality of people. They seem to be of a different order from myself."

"She does not want one of the same order," said Alice, aside. "She was explaining it to Miss Burke."

"It grieves me, Mother," said Rosebery, "that you should want a companion of any kind, when you have two able and willing men at your disposal."

"That is why I want one. I am old and weak, and able men do not meet my need. I am twelve years older than your father, and I have resolved never to be a burden on him. The time has come to avoid it. I want someone who will adapt herself to me and accept my words and ways. It is not much to ask in return for what she will be given."

"Can Aunt Miranda mean what she says?" said Francis.

"She should advertise for a martyr," said his sister. "But I suppose she has done so. She wants a companion, and the two things are known to be the same."

"What are you whispering about?" said Miranda. "You are too old to get into corners and snigger like stable boys. When you are given a home like this, the least you can do is to deserve it."

"People seem to have to do a good deal for a home,"

said Alice. "And it does not seem an unnatural thing to have."

"You have a right to this one," said Julius. "You are my brother's children."

"But not your own," said Miranda. "They tend to forget that."

"It is the last thing I want them to remember."

"I did not know that stable boys sniggered," said Alice. "They always seem so grave."

"They certainly swear very earnestly," said her brother.

"Francis, I have never heard it," said Rosebery, on a note of consternation.

"They know what is fit for your ears," said Julius.

"I do not disclaim the suggestion that I should be discountenanced by it, Father. Swearing and the like are no part of manliness to me."

"We have seen they are the part of stable boys."

"It seems that several things are," said Francis.

Miranda did not look disturbed. She did not grudge the children their affinity with her husband, or resent its being greater than her son's. It was the meaning of her life that Rosebery should belong to herself. Between the mother and son there vibrated an active emotion, that the children took for granted, and Julius met with dry acceptance. Rosebery poured out on Miranda all his feeling for womanhood, which was the thing that chiefly occupied his thoughts.

The last person to share them thanked him at the door, received his half-sorrowful disclaimer and went into the library. She was received by Bates in a manner equally suggestive of attendant and hostess.

"So you did not come to an understanding, miss?"

"Yes, we did and soon. Mrs. Hume said I should not suit her."

"It is not everyone who would suit the mistress," said Bates, standing with her rising nose and beetling brow seeming to glow with self-complacence, while her small, honest, black eyes actually did so. "It is not for me to judge, and what is not for me is omitted in my case. But having suited her since the year eighteen sixty, my words speak."

"I did not suit her for as many minutes. And she did not suit me as long. I do not envy the thirty-seven years."

"Oh, you will secure a position, miss," said Bates, in recognition of this spirit. "I entertain no doubt. And if it was ordained, it was to be."

"I wish I had known it was ordained, in time to be spared the interview. Happily it was short."

"Short and sharp," agreed Bates, as if she visualised it. "It was not prolonged."

"Mrs. Hume thought I should profit by it. I think she even hoped I should. She seemed to wish me well in her way."

"There is her bell," said Bates. "I am used to exactions. I must leave you for the moment."

She did so, and Miss Burke looked about her without curiosity. She seldom felt it, as she attached no importance to what she saw. She had learned that the setting of human experience was no key to itself.

Bates returned and continued, as if no break had occurred.

"There is another position in the neighbourhood, miss; as housekeeper to two single ladies; on a smaller scale, but not enough to be a detriment."

"I would rather be with two women than with a married couple and a family," said Miss Burke, as though the latter struck her as an abnormal situation, as possibly it did.

"One can feel among the superfluous," said Bates. "Which is not as it should be, the truth being otherwise."

"I suppose one has to be that. It is a condition of being needed. No one wants a person who is necessary to someone else."

"Which is deep," said Bates. "Well, I hope we shall meet again. We share the dignity of earning bread."

"If dignity is what it is. I should prefer other kinds of it."

"I will give you the ladies' address, miss. It is some stations along the line. You could mention that I sent you. The houses do not visit, but my name will speak."

Bates accompanied Miss Burke to the door, but found she was anticipated. Rosebery stood ready to open it, and having done so, took his hat from the stand and stepped after the stranger out of the house.

"You would not ask me to countenance your walking alone in the dusk? It would indeed be much to expect."

"It is very kind of you, Mr. Hume."

"Rather is it a matter of course and a privilege. It may happen that the two things coincide."

"The days are shortening, but I am not a nervous person."

"It is an eerie road," said Rosebery, glancing behind him in a manner that precluded his making a similar claim. "I do not lose that impression, familiar though I am with it."

"I am not troubled by eeriness. I am concerned with more definite things."

"But for ladies the vaguer ones have their menace."

"Well, men may be inclined to think so."

"And may be right," said Rosebery, who went further than this and enjoyed the thought. "It is easy to imagine footsteps behind one, when they are echoes of one's own."

He proved his words when he turned homewards, and hastened his steps until he had escaped from the pursuing echoes into the house.

"Where have you been?" said Miranda.

"Along the road as far as the village, Mother."

"With Miss Burke?"

"With whom else? Who but her was in a similar plight?"

"You looked disturbed when you came in," said Francis.

"And I was disturbed, Francis, or had been so. By the idea of a woman walking alone along a deserted road at dusk. I accompanied her as far as the houses, where the lights begin."

"And had to come back by yourself," said Julius.

"Well, naturally, Father. I could hardly expect her to perform the same office for me. It would have been a case of our going to and fro 'ad infinitum.' "

"One of the boys could have gone with her," said Miranda.

"But one of the boys did not offer to, Mother. So the privilege fell to me. And I can claim that I found it such."

"You have a lofty character," said Francis.

"Well, I hope an ordinary manly one."

"There seems little difference," said Alice.

"Perhaps there should not be too much," said her cousin.

"Bates, what did Miss Burke say to you?" said Miranda, who changed the talk at will.

"There were casual words, ma'am."

"Did she speak about me?"

"Well, ma'am, she alluded to the outcome."

"What else did you talk about?"

"Topics arose, ma'am."

"Where was she going after this?"

"There is a position, ma'am, in the vicinity."

"You mean she is going to apply for it?"

"Well, to appraise it, ma'am."

"Was she upset by my refusing her?"

"Well, ma'am, it was in the course of things."

"Did she have a good tea?"

"I trust she was refreshed, ma'am."

"That is not what I asked you."

"There was the cake and bread-and-butter, ma'am."

"Well, was not that enough?"

"We cannot know to what she is accustomed, ma'am."

"I know exactly; but I should know more than you; it would be strange if I did not. Now surely you children should go to your books? Mr. Pettigrew comes this afternoon. We do not go to the expense of a tutor, to have you fritter away your time."

"We do not do much for him," said Francis. "We allow his progress to be slow. He has made a good deal since he came to us."

"Is he an expensive tutor?" said Adrian.

"Expensive enough for a penniless boy," said his aunt.

"He is the only tutor in the neighbourhood," said Julius. "It is a very cheap way of having you taught."

"I am glad of that," said Francis. "It is as it ought to be."

"I am sometimes troubled about it. But it means I have you at home."

"I have sometimes thought of returning to the pupillary status myself," said Rosebery, "and refreshing my early memories. One is never too old to learn."

"That is untrue," said Francis. "People are soon too old. That is how pupils catch up their teachers."

"You implied that your teacher was engaged in catching up you," said Miranda.

"You must admit, Francis," said Rosebery, "that my mother is the logician on this occasion, far though it is from being the reputation of her sex."

"Well, go and catch up Mr. Pettigrew as quickly as you can," said Miranda. "We have had enough of you down here."

"Are you really catching him up?" said Adrian to his brother and sister on the stairs, not entertaining the idea of himself.

"We do not consider so low an ambition," said Francis.

"He is waiting for us," said Alice. "I saw his hat in the hall. It is a good thing Aunt Miranda did not."

"I wonder she did not feel it was there. I think there were signs that she almost did."

CHAPTER II

"It would be nicer, Miss Alice," said Mr. Pettigrew, "if you did not make faces when my back is turned."

This statement, though there seemed no reason to dispute it, caused an outbreak of mirth from the hearers.

"It would indeed have been nicer, if it had happened like that," said Francis under his breath.

"Now I have observed before," said Mr. Pettigrew, "that there is no point in meaningless hilarity. When a gentleman is constrained to make a criticism, it is only polite to accept it. Now can you tell me what you are laughing at now?"

His pupils could not tell him that it was his manner of alluding to himself.

"Well, I shall not ask you," he said, perhaps warned by experience. "It would lead to frivolity and waste of time. Will you begin to construe, Miss Alice?"

The latter did so, with less than average success.

"Have you prepared this?"

"No," said Alice, unsteadily.

"How did you spend the time assigned to your work?"

Alice made no reply.

"Do I assume that you wasted it in idle talk?"

"I don't know if you do."

"How old are you now, if I may ask?"

"Thirteen and a half."

"Then your brothers are fifteen and twelve. You are too old for this flightiness and irresponsibility. It is not fair to your parents or to me."

"We have no parents," said Alice.

"To those who stand to you in their stead. To your aunt and uncle, who afford you every advantage. Now there can be no reasonable cause for amusement there." Mr. Pettigrew flushed, as he realised the actual cause. "We will proceed to our work, and I hope there will be less frivolity; no more indeed than if your aunt were present."

The next outbreak was induced by the latter's entrance, as it resulted in the boys' rising to their feet and Mr. Pettigrew's failing to do so. Miranda looked as if she understood it, and did not wholly disapprove.

"Well, how are they getting on, Mr. Pettigrew?"

"I think the progress is satisfactory, Mrs. Hume, in spite of occasional unsteadiness. I should say that the standard is up to their ages and maintained at that level. And I make a point of adding to my own knowledge, as we advance."

There was mirth at this admission, as the pupils' view

of the tutor did not prevent their regarding omniscience as due from him.

"They are silly children," said Miranda. "I fear they must try your patience."

"Our relation has been long enough to result in mutual understanding," said Mr. Pettigrew, with truth.

Miranda went to the door, and Francis opened it for her, Mr. Pettigrew moving in his seat to allow him to do so, and keeping his eyes on his books until it closed.

"I did not mention, Adrian, that your standard is relatively lower than your brother and sister's. I hope we may remedy the position and avoid the disclosure."

"He is not on our level," said Francis.

"Yes I am," said his brother. "I am only different."

"And that is what the difference consists in."

"It is that in which the difference consists," said Mr. Pettigrew. "We do not end a sentence with a preposition."

"Great writers do not worry about that sort of thing," said Alice.

"Well, when you join their ranks, you can follow their example. Until then we will observe the accepted usage."

Mr. Pettigrew was a small, neat, middle-aged man, with careful, dark clothes and hair and beard, features that fulfilled their purpose, and small, blue, spectacled eyes, that tended to light with curiosity. As a thought occurred to him, they did so.

"You have had a visitor this afternoon. I saw your cousin accompanying a lady to the station. I should say to the village, but as the directions coincide, it occurred to me that the station might be their object."

"Aunt Miranda wanted a companion," said Francis. "But when she saw her, she changed her mind. And everyone but Rosebud thought the matter had ended."

"Your cousin certainly followed his own course. I noticed he was showing the stranger the same degree of attention, as if their positions had been reversed."

"Why should he show her any less?" said Alice.

"He saw no reason. That is why he merits the description."

"Rosebud should have been a woman," said Francis, "he takes so much interest in them. Or perhaps it is the last thing he should have been."

"Do you like opening doors for women?" said Adrian to the tutor.

There was a pause before the latter spoke with a faint flush.

"I think, Adrian, that you and your brother might use the term, 'sir', in addressing me. There seems no reason to deviate from the usual custom."

"Alice does not say it."

"Convention does not require it, or indeed permit it, in her case. I was referring to you and Francis, as I made clear. Now what was your question?"

"I asked if you liked opening doors for women?" said Adrian, not using the suggested mode of address, as it seemed to him to have a menial significance.

"I hope I have the proper feelings on such occasions, those of a normal gentleman. I trust I do not let such opportunities pass. It would not be so, unless through absence of mind. I think that is a fair claim to make on my own behalf."

"Rosebud opens the door for Aunt Miranda, as if it were the first time in his life," said Francis.

"There are some feelings that never lose their freshness, if the possessors of them are fortunate. I cannot but realise whom you indicate by your abbreviation, and it is perhaps not inconsistent with your youthful view of your cousin. But we will proceed to our work, before we accuse ourselves of wasting time."

The accusation was to come from another quarter. Miranda ordered tea for Mr. Pettigrew, in the belief that it would stimulate his efforts; and on this occasion, when Bates entered with the tray, her mistress followed her.

"Well, you hardly seem to have settled down to work."

"We always make up any time we have missed, Mrs. Hume. I find that effort is easier to me, when I have had the tea you considerately provide. I can say I have never curtailed the appointed time."

"Well, I suppose you have not. It would be natural to work the full time, and necessary for the children's progress."

"And that is great enough to preclude that manner of referring to them, though I may always be likely to return to it in my thoughts."

"I hope it does not give you too low a standard for them. The boys must make their own way. We are anxious for them to get on."

"On the contrary, Mrs. Hume, it gives me a standard

higher in proportion to my feeling for them, which I
may claim to have become almost paternal."

"Is that the second of those two plain cakes?" said
Miranda to Bates.

"Yes, ma'am. We finished the other—the other was
finished when the lady had tea in the library."

"You meant what you said at first, I think. One person could hardly have eaten what was left of that cake.
And we never have the plain kind in the drawing
room."

The children recognised with amusement the standing of the provision for the tutor. His continuing to
think of them in this way had some excuse.

"I am not proposing to attack the cake today, Mrs.
Hume. Mrs. Pettigrew provides so many cakes for me,
also of the plain variety, as that happens to be my
preference, that I am inclined to confine myself to the
bread-and-butter, as a viand of which one never tires."

"You generally have some cake, I think," said
Miranda, whose claim that she saw into every corner of
her house was open and just. "And I hope that you do,
if you enjoy it, and that you will continue to do so. I am
glad you like the kind our custom assigns to the schoolroom."

"I have no doubt that I enjoy it, Mrs. Hume, if I
happen to take a piece unawares, as I may when my
thoughts are elsewhere. I believe it is possible to enjoy
a thing without knowing it."

"No, I hardly think it is," said Miranda, handing him
the cake. "Why not take a piece now, and enjoy it and
know that you are doing so?"

Mr. Pettigrew took a piece without looking at it, and put it on his plate, as though he must put it somewhere. He watched Adrian attend his aunt to the door, with an air of superintendence, and then opened a book and made some comment upon it. When a break occurred, he looked up.

"So the stranger who was here this afternoon, is not to take your aunt's post?"

"She was not offered it," said Francis. "She did not find favour in her sight. But she did not betray any feeling."

"Am I to understand that the interview took place in the general view?" said Mr. Pettigrew, dropping his eyes to veil his disapproval.

"Yes, Aunt Miranda did not trouble to go to another room."

"I was making no suggestion regarding your aunt. But surely you young people could and should have withdrawn."

"We were told to keep at a distance and appear to be occupied. And there was nothing to engage us but the scene. Uncle stayed by the window, and Rosebud was allowed to remain where he was. He would have had the best of it, if he had not been so affected by what happened."

"I think I find myself in accord with your cousin. It is a great test of personal quality to face rebuff of that kind without self-betrayal. I think we should estimate it at its worth."

"Pettigrew has had such rebuffs himself," said Alice, more audibly than she knew.

"No, Miss Alice," said Mr. Pettigrew, smiling indulgently, "my upward path has been on the whole smooth. I hope the same will be true of your brothers."

"So he sees us as on his level," murmured Francis.

"It is true that our circumstances have something in common. But, to be serious for a moment, I think we should view such a person as we are discussing, with all respect and sympathy."

"I hardly think we do," said Alice. "We admire success."

"Well, we have all had a modicum of that," said Mr. Pettigrew, smiling again. "But success does not impose the same demand, or so I have found from my modest experience of it."

"It makes a demand on other people," said Adrian. "They have to be pleased by it, when it does nothing for them."

"You and I will not put them to the test," said Alice. "We shall be overshadowed by Francis. He will be an elder son, even though an impoverished one."

"And that means he can never really be impoverished."

"Stay, Miss Alice. Are you condemning your cousin to perpetual bachelorhood?"

"It is his own resolve and choice," said Francis. "All his feeling is given to his mother."

"But in the nature of things that state of affairs must cease."

"He has put it into words. And that is so rare that he must be believed. He will be faithful to her memory."

"You cannot depend on it, Francis," said Mr. Pettigrew, in troubled warning. "Many people misjudge the permanent effect of sorrow, and their capacity to live in the past. And it is not a course to be wished for them. For example, if I had followed it, Mrs. Pettigrew and I should have missed much happiness; and it is hard to see how it would have benefited those who had gone before."

"It benefits those who are to come after," said Alice. "In this case it is Francis. And Rosebud will have what he wants. He will think of Aunt Miranda as existing, and appreciating his faithfulness."

"But would she appreciate it, Miss Alice? Would she not choose him to be happy and fulfilled in the normal way? If I were a mother—that is rather a feat of imagination, and I see you find it so—if I held any intimate relation to a younger person, I should wish to benefit him without exacting sacrifice to my memory. And I venture to think your aunt would feel as I do."

A sound of amusement confirmed this view as venturesome.

"She does nothing like anyone else," said Alice.

"As the applicant for her post would probably concur," said Mr. Pettigrew, smiling. "But I should hardly have judged from your cousin's demeanour towards her that he was likely to be vowed to bachelorhood. Not that I suggest any especial feeling towards the person in question. The idea had not occurred to me; and it would involve discrepancies that do not concern us."

"Pettigrew will go any length rather than refer to the companion as a lady," murmured Alice.

"And yet he refers to himself in the corresponding way," said Francis.

"What did you say, Miss Alice?"

"Nothing. Nothing that had any meaning."

"I caught my own name and the word, 'companion', and fail to see what connection there is between us."

His pupils yielded to mirth, as the question did not find them at a loss.

"Well, we will resume our work. It was a mistake to interrupt it. I fear the blame is mine."

The remaining time passed without disturbance, and the tutor apportioned the tasks and took his leave. The pupils at once relaxed.

"What is the meaning of our life?" said Francis. "To keep Pettigrew from want?"

"What will he do when we are grown-up?" said Adrian.

"I suppose he will suffer the want."

"And his wife and family with him," said Alice, smiling at the wider possibility.

"Shall we ever have to teach, as he does?" said Adrian. "Perhaps Aunt Miranda will be dead, and Uncle will be willing to support us."

"So you have death in your heart," said Francis.

"I should not do anything to make her die. And she has never wanted us to live at all. She is worse than I am."

"Alice, we must remember that Adrian is our brother. Should not our combined influence do something for him? Is it our fault that it has failed so far?"

"What is this?" said Bates, coming in on some quest. "Now, have you been teasing him?"

"I wish Nurse had not gone," said Adrian. "It was because Aunt Miranda would not pay her."

"Now that is an ungrateful way to talk. And you know Bates is always here."

"Why should we talk gratefully?" said Alice. "Nurse has not stayed."

"Bates, Alice made faces at Pettigrew, and he saw her," said Adrian.

"What nonsense! Of course I did not."

"It was the reflection of your face on hers, that gave the illusion," said Francis.

"Now if I leave you, will you see he does not tease him?" said Bates, feeling no need to be more specific.

"Don't speak to him, unless I give you permission," said Alice to Francis, in an incidental tone.

Adrian relapsed in the manner of a person protected. "Do we have an empty life?" he said.

"Well, that is fair enough," said Alice. "We don't save anyone else's from emptiness."

"I think we should save Uncle's, if it were not for Aunt Miranda."

"Why think of the might-have-beens?" said Francis.

"It is strange that she and Rosebery like each other, when no one else likes either of them."

"Uncle feels they are his wife and son."

"He knows it, if he does not feel it," said Alice.

"He feels it about Aunt Miranda," said Adrian. "That is the reason of everything."

The tutor met Julius and his son in the hall, and paused with a flush and start.

"Good-evening, Mr. Hume."

"How are you, Pettigrew?" said Julius, shaking hands. "I hope my young ones do not trouble you. Remember me to your wife."

"Thank you, Mr. Hume, I will certainly do so. And she would wish me to give you a similar message. Good-evening, Mr. Rosebery; it is a chilly night; I hope you have been able to remain indoors."

"Good-evening, Mr. Pettigrew," said Rosebery, with a full smile and handshake. "I have been out on a mission of my own, but have otherwise been unoccupied. I fear I should be called a less useful person than you."

"Oh, I do not know. There are many kinds of usefulness."

"Too many," said Julius. "It results in a workaday world. Goodbye again. We keep early hours, and my wife is firm about them."

"Goodbye, Mr. Hume. Mrs. Pettigrew is of a similar mind. Indeed she finds inexactitude about hours more trying than the more serious shortcomings; though the lack of consideration involved should perhaps place it among those."

Mr. Pettigrew put on his hat and coat with a consciousness that eyes were on him, and Julius withdrew his own and turned to the dining-room.

"There are exceptions to human inconsistency. Pettigrew can only be himself."

"He was concerned for Miss Burke," said Francis, "indeed moved by her position."

"Well, it is really the same as his," said Alice.

"We should all have a fellow-feeling for those who

are in it," said Rosebery. "Think how easily we might be in it ourselves."

"I was thinking it," said Francis, "and it will indeed be easy."

"I am not sure I have not missed something in being placed beyond, or shall we say apart from such necessity. It might bring out qualities now unsuspected."

"Has nothing aroused your own suspicions?" said Julius.

"How mean of people not to suspect them!" said Alice. "It is not a thing we should be left to do for ourselves."

"People's qualities are clear," said Miranda, looking from her son to her nephews, as if she saw an illustration of this. "There is no occasion to suspect them."

"But I think my mother does suspect them in my case," said Rosebery, smiling. "And I feel it is a natural situation between a mother and a son. If you three had had a mother, which I know not to have been the case, I should not have to suggest that."

"We have not had one, whom we can remember," said Francis.

"You have not, Francis. And often have I found my heart bleed for you on that ground. I think the little beliefs and blindnesses between two people so near to each other, are not the least of the things that we may have, and that you have missed."

"Everything must be forgiven us," said Alice. "We can never be to blame. Pettigrew ought to know about it."

"Father," said Rosebery, "I have often meant to ask

you if you remember my cousins' mother, and if you see
any resemblance in them to her. It is a matter of interest to me. I do not know why it has hitherto escaped
my memory."

"Because it was not of enough interest to you. I
remember her well. We were intimate with each other.
Adrian and Alice remind me of her, though they are all
more like their father."

"And so like you, Father, a thing I cannot claim to
be."

"Perhaps my face is my fortune," said Adrian, "as I
have no other."

"The first can hardly be said of me," said Rosebery,
with his slow laugh. "Perhaps it is as well that the
second cannot either."

"Your appearance does us credit," said Francis,
looking at his cousin's evening clothes. "You know
what is due to yourself."

"Rather do I know, Francis, what is due to my
mother's presence. As I have said, I am protected from
the imputation of personal vanity."

"Appearance has not much to do with that," said
Julius.

"Well, well, you know your own reasons for dressing,
Father."

"Why should they not be the same as yours?"

"Father, I am sure they are," said Rosebery, with
grave compunction. "I must plead guilty to speaking
with levity. The companionship of my young cousins
may dispose me to it."

"It does not have any great success," said Alice.

"Does it not?" said Rosebery. "I sometimes find an idle note creeping into my talk, that is not natural to it."

"I suppose Miss Burke is at home by now?" said Miranda. "I don't know where she lives."

"Then how can you assume she has arrived there?" said Julius.

"I understood her to say she had no home," said Rosebery, on a faintly reproachful note. "And she was to visit another house in the neighbourhood before ending her day."

"To apply for another post?" said Miranda.

"That is the presumption, Mother. Our acquaintance did not warrant my putting the question. But she had, if I may so express it, the light of battle in her eye."

"It was very late to go anywhere. What will the people think?"

"If they think what I do, they will estimate the spirit that carries her on in the face of convention and discouragement," said Rosebery, with the light also appearing in his.

"She ought to have been your companion," said Alice.

"Well, she was so for a suitable period," said Rosebery, smiling.

"Pettigrew took a great interest in her," said Francis. "He saw you escorting her to the village, and was full of curiosity."

"There is a freemasonry between these people," said Miranda.

"Now, Mother, whom do you include in that term?

I should not have applied the same to the two in question."

"Other people would. Unless you mean that one is a woman."

"It seems strange that you will never see Miss Burke again," said Adrian to his cousin.

"I gave the conclusion of the matter in my own words: 'a ship that passed in the night'."

"The boys need not have that wine," said Miranda, as she rose from the table. "Do not ply them with it, Julius. They must not depend on such things. They are only downstairs because the kitchenmaid is away."

"As I am accused of giving preference to women," said Rosebery, also rising, "I will deserve the reputation and indulge the propensity. I do not grudge my cousins my share of the wine, which to me means nothing."

"Rosebery will marry some woman one day," said Francis. "I don't see how he can avoid it. Unless through the impossibility of marrying all women."

"Aunt Miranda does not know that the heart supposed to be hers is so divided," said Alice.

"She seems to know everything," said Adrian.

"Well, she may see it as a safeguard. If he liked one woman, she would lose him. If he liked none, she would never have had him."

"So you know everything too," said Francis.

"Yes, I have caught it from Aunt Miranda. And Adrian has begun to. It is a poor foundation for earning his bread. Suppose she had to earn hers! She does not know how bad her influence has been."

Julius listened to his nephews and niece in silence.

He never checked the use of their wits or noticed the signs of inexperience. He accepted the mingled precocity and childishness that was the result of their life.

"We ought to know a little of one thing and rise to fame," said Francis. "Eminent people always explain how many things they don't know; and how little they know of the one thing, indeed how little is known of it."

"What if one knows a little of a good many things?" said Adrian. "That is how it would usually be."

"Then one is like Pettigrew," said Alice, "and able to earn a living. It is a good thing it is usual."

"We will share this wine," said Julius. "I will not drink it alone, and Rosebery does not know it from any other."

"And admires himself for it," said Francis. "How people admire themselves for everything! I find it hard to do so."

"And admire yourself for it," said his sister.

"Well, it is something to be a human being," said Adrian, "and be better than other creatures."

"You need not put your glass down, Adrian," said Miranda's voice. "I presume you do not do behind my back what you would not do to my face; so you may go on with what you are doing."

Adrian did not comply, and Miranda kept her eyes on him.

"Go on with your wine. If you can drink it when I am not here, you can do so in my presence."

Adrian raised the glass to his lips.

"I suppose the truth is that you cannot drink it at all.

You wanted to be independent and sophisticated. Well, are you having your wish?"

"Adrian is called upon to be other things," murmured Francis.

"We were saying you knew everything, Miranda," said Julius. "And it appears we were right."

"Well, I knew what was happening here. I did not see your faces, when I spoke about the wine, without foreseeing that. I am not an easy person to deceive."

"And you came back to catch us in the act?"

"Or to give you the chance of showing me my mistake. You have not taken it."

"No, we have not your gift of foresight."

"So I can trust no one. No one but my son. Not my husband, not the children whom I took into my house as homeless babes. What would have been their fate, if I had not?"

"What it has been," said her husband. "I should have taken them in. This house is mine and their natural home. But you have done well by them, and enabled me to do better. We are all grateful to you."

"You seem to feel nearer to them than to your son."

"They are more of my nature. No father has had a son more unlike himself. I gave Rosebery up to you. Indeed I think you took him."

"He was a man when the children came to us. You were never to him what you have been to them."

"He was not the child I had thought of. And these children gave me back my boyhood. I was helpless in the matter. So were you; so were they."

"And so was he," said Miranda, her voice deepening.

"He has never had a father. Few sons would have for-given it as he has."

"And had I not things to forgive? Did he not take what was mine, my place in your heart and in your life? Few fathers would have yielded it as I have."

"Your yielding it tells its tale. I had to give him what I could; or what would he have had? And he has given it back to me. He would not betray my trust. He would not do little wrong things behind my back; he would not do them any more than the great ones; and that is a rare thing."

"I believe it is. And it is true that he would not do them."

"He would not make me afraid to go about in my own house," said Miranda, turning away as if no more could be said.

"I wish she did not overcome the fear," said Francis.

"Oh, you do, do you, Francis?" said his aunt, opening the door. "Only you or your sister would have said that. I did not give you the shelter of my roof, to nourish a viper under it." She ended on a suggestively hissing note and closed the door.

"People generally nourish vipers in a more intimate place," said Francis, uneasily.

"Aunt Miranda has not done so," said Alice. "And she would not make the claim."

"What a day of embarrassments!" said her brother. "The companion rejected with insult; Rosebery be-traying that his heart was wrung; Pettigrew discon-certed over the cake at tea; and now our own dis-comfiture."

"So it is true that comedy and tragedy are mingled," said Adrian.

"Really it is all tragedy," said his sister. "Comedy is a wicked way of looking at it, when it is not our own."

"Is that why people cannot laugh at themselves?" said Julius.

"This last trouble was our own," said Adrian.

"Yes, and it was all tragedy," said Alice. "What really good person could have a sense of humour? We see that Rosebery has none."

"What happened about the cake at tea?" said Julius.

The children gave him their account of it, perhaps illustrating the theory that no good person could have a sense of humour; and in the midst of it Miranda returned, crossed the room without looking at them, took something from the sideboard and left them without a word.

"Yes, life is all tragedy," said Francis. "It would be shocking to see its comic side."

Julius followed his wife to the drawing-room, where the children's presence was not permitted at night. Rosebery got up from the seat opposite his mother's.

"No, this chair will do for me. You may keep your place."

"I am not entitled to use those words of it, Father. I usurped it in your absence."

"You look tired, Miranda. Things have been too much for you to-day."

"Yes, I am tired. I am old and weak. And servants and children and tutors have done their work."

"Will not a companion be something more on the list?"

"She will identify her interests with mine. That will be the purpose of her. And she will relieve you and the children of the brunt of me."

"I am glad, Mother, that you do not include my name," said Rosebery. "The brunt of you is not a thing I am concerned to avoid."

"Your father does not say the same."

"I do not say things that are suggested. They would have no meaning. And I recognise that Rosebery does better than I."

"Are you taking any further step towards the companion, Mother?"

"I am leaving the advertisement in the local paper."

"That all may know your need," said her husband.

"Yes, Mother, it does not redound to our credit," said Rosebery, in a tone of expostulation. "I enter a definite protest against the scheme."

"If the right person comes, I can take her. If the wrong, I am committed to nothing."

"You can deal with her as you did with her predecessor," said Julius.

"I am hardly disposed to be present at the scene," said his son.

"You will allow the next applicant to dispense with your services?"

"I did not say that, Father. I could be at hand, in case she had need of them. I should do nothing for her by witnessing her cross-examination and possible discomfiture; and if I may say so, you could not either. I should venture to recommend your withdrawal."

"I am inclined to take your advice. To-day I had no warning."

"And will not on another day," said his wife. "It is the last thing that would occur to me. What a fuss to make about nothing! What does the companion's reaction matter?"

"I feared that was your view, Mother," said Rosebery, in a tone at once amused and grieved. "And I must admit I take the opposite one. It seems to me that the feelings of an unprotected woman matter as much as anything in life."

"She would be used to being questioned and cutting an indifferent figure," said Miranda, easily.

"I cannot think that is a thing to which any of us could get used."

"Anyone would think I was an ogress, and the companion a martyr."

"I think that might be a possible view of the position, Mother."

"There is never much in the conventional views of these things. Some people are more fortunately placed in life than others. That is how it sums up."

"Many things sum up in that way," said Julius.

"And yet there is something to be said for existing conditions," said Rosebery. "There must be hewers of wood and drawers of water. There, Mother, there is a definition for you of a companion. You did not give it to Miss Burke."

"I think she almost did," said Julius.

"I hope, Mother," said Rosebery, with a note of distress, as if struck by a misgiving, "that you will not use my words in your next interview. It would be playing me unfairly indeed. Not that you have not in a way a claim to them. Requiring someone to wash dishes may be said to involve her drawing water." He leaned back in mirth.

CHAPTER III

"Good-morning, Miss Greatheart," said Miss Burke.

"Good-morning, dear," said the former, with an affection that seemed to bear out her name, after a day's acquaintance. "How nice it is to have you here! And look at the breakfast you have made for us. How clever it is to cook and plan and be indispensable to everyone! It is no good to wish I were like you."

Miss Burke hardly felt that it was, as she completed her work at the table. She did not look at the breakfast, as she had nothing to learn about it, but simply regarded Miss Greatheart in an amiable manner. This household bore no likeness to Mrs. Hume's.

"Shall I go upstairs and call Miss Wolsey?"

"No, dear, ring the bell and spare yourself the trouble," said Miss Greatheart, in a tone that vibrated with concern. "And then sit down and help yourself. There is no need for you to have your breakfast cold, because I am so careless of such things. I believe I could live on a desert island and eat grain and be content."

Miss Burke, who did not share the belief, and might not have cooked the breakfast if she had, rang the bell and came to the table, and Miss Greatheart followed her.

"Well, Plautus," she said, "so you are full of wisdom. Full of great thoughts on everything. You would not deign to say good-morning to us. We are beneath your notice."

Plautus walked smoothly to the fire and sat down and regarded it.

"No, he will not say good-morning to us, Hester," said Miss Greatheart, as her friend appeared. "He will sit and enjoy his reflections and ignore you and me."

Plautus turned his attention to a feather that stirred on the floor.

"He is a beautiful cat," said Miss Burke, willing to take her part.

"So you do not care for cats, dear," said Miss Greatheart, turning to her in swift understanding.

"I like to look at them," said Miss Burke, uncertain what her words might imply.

"Oh, Plautus, what does she say?" said Miss Wolsey.

"I said I liked to look at him," said Miss Burke, not meeting her eyes.

"Well, how could you not? Surely that goes without saying."

Miss Burke was silent, as silence could serve to this extent.

"So she forgets your wisdom and wit, Plautus," said Miss Greatheart, leaning towards the latter without gaining his eye.

"I do not see how a cat can have wit," said Miss Burke, who was accustomed to hold her own, and found it the best policy.

"Oh, he has made several bright remarks to me this morning," said Miss Wolsey. "He came into my room in quite a facetious spirit. I could hardly keep up with him."

"Favouritism!" said Miss Greatheart, shaking her head. "He did not come into mine. He has given no proof that he recognises me this morning."

"Why do you call him 'Plautus'?" said Miss Burke, encouraged by this simple statement of truth.

"Oh, because he *is* Plautus," said Miss Wolsey. "Because the essence of Plautus is in him. How could he be called anything else?"

"Who was Plautus in real life?"

"Who could he have been but the person to give this Plautus his name?"

"He was a Latin writer," said Miss Greatheart, as Miss Burke left a second question unanswered. "I think he wrote plays; not very good ones."

"Why did you call the cat after him?"

"Well, he has not written any good plays either," said Miss Wolsey, holding out her hand to Plautus, who came and considered it, as if in the hope of some offering.

"You think we are a silly trio, don't you dear?" said Miss Greatheart.

Miss Burke took a moment to determine the third member of the group.

"You would not expect me to call Plautus silly?"

"Well, I think you have led us to expect it. How

you despise us all, and how we shall admire you for it!
We look up to people who look down on us. It is hard to
see how we could avoid it, though I think Plautus does."

Emma Greatheart gave the impression that everything about her was moulded on a generous scale, and
that she did not dispute it or wish it otherwise. Her
large, curved frame, full, grey eyes, lofty, aquiline
features and undisguised marks of sixty years contributed to the effect, and her flowing garments accorded
with the air of amplitude. Her large, fine hands looked
as if they might be capable, if their owner willed it, but
as if she did not do so.

Hester Wolsey was eleven years younger and looked
spare beside her, though above the average size. She
had dark, solid features and a general aspect of hand-
someness that had gained her the name. The emotions
of her deep, eager eyes were under her control. Her
clothes were as successful and costly as she could con-
trive.

"No, you are not hungry, Plautus. You need not
show that wistful face."

"He has not finished his saucer of milk," said Miss
Burke, who had supplied him in this manner when he
crossed her path.

"He does not drink much milk," said Hester, disturbing her ideas. "But he knows there is fish for breakfast; so he does, the wise, wise man."

Plautus walked to the table and stood with his face
raised towards it.

"So he heard what you said," said Emma, in a
generous tone.

Miss Burke hardly felt she could deny it.

"Yes, you heard it indeed," said Hester, speaking with her eyes on the cat. "You do not let a word of mine escape you."

"One has to be quite careful what one says," said Emma, suggesting the scope of Plautus's attention.

Miss Burke, with an idea of establishing her position, offered Plautus a piece of fish.

"No, no, dear," said Emma, leaning forward. "You will spoil his manners."

Miss Burke looked up in question.

"His beautiful manners," said Hester, bringing her no enlightenment. "Must not eat at meals."

"When does he eat?" said Miss Burke.

"You did not know that Plautus had manners, did you dear?" said Emma, in sympathy. "You don't understand a cat's code."

Miss Burke rose to remove the fish.

"Let me help you, dear," said Emma, earnestly, leaning back in her chair.

Miss Burke carried the dish from the room, and Plautus, following the code referred to, unobtrusively followed her. Both ladies looked at her as she returned.

"Did you give him any fish?" said Hester.

"Yes, a great, big piece," said Miss Burke, with a sense of catching the authentic note. "And he ate it all up; so he did, the understanding man."

There was a pause that made her feel she had overreached.

"He will think you are making advances to him," said Emma, in a neutral tone.

"He is not a cupboard lover," said Hester. "He does not respond to bribes. Only real love for Plautus."

"He will never get as fond of me as he is of you," said Miss Burke, incautiously answering the thought behind the words.

"Plautus is fond of two people and no more. He does not dissipate his feeling. He will not welcome titbits from any hand but ours."

Plautus returned to the room, paused for a moment by Miss Burke and proceeded to the fire.

"Ah, he is an actor," said Hester. "He pretends he is like other cats, but he does not deceive us."

"He deceived me," said Miss Burke. "I do not see any difference."

"Oh, naughty Plautus to deceive! Yes, you know you were doing it."

"Well, Plautus, will you come with me to the kitchen? We shall soon understand each other, though you need more study than I thought."

Plautus rose, looked earnestly at Miss Burke's tray, and again accompanied her.

"He is a greedy puss," said Emma, as though not repudiating truth.

"He is too kind to make differences between people," said Hester. "But he knows them in his heart."

"Now, Plautus, keep out of my way," said Miss Burke, as she reached the kitchen. "I don't want you round my legs while I am at work."

Plautus approached and rubbed himself against the limbs in question.

"You understand nothing. You have no thoughts and

no feelings. You are interested only in yourself, and you give me the shudders. You can remember it."

Plautus raised his face towards her.

"You will get nothing more until you have finished your milk. I don't like wastefulness, and I will not have it in a cat. Milk is your food, unless you are a wild beast. That is the truth about you."

"Does he really upset you, dear?" said Emma, on Miss Burke's return, as if she had divined this passage.

"No, of course he does not. He and I will be the best of friends. He is a beautiful cat."

"Ah, the lady does not like you, Plautus. You must promise me not to worry her. Now look me in the face and promise."

Emma held Plautus up before her, and he looked at nothing while he awaited his release, and on gaining it began to wash, as though to rid himself of some contamination.

"He is always licking himself," said Miss Burke, in an equivocal tone.

"Yes, cats are the cleanest of creatures," said Hester, in agreement.

"I know, dear, I know," said Emma, leaning forward and laying her hand on Miss Burke's. "Your heart is given to dogs."

"I do not like animals in the house at all," said Miss Burke, who was true to herself, and therefore perhaps could not be false to any man. "They are in the way and they make extra work."

"And you have had enough work, you poor, dear, useful one. You must be so proud, and think we should

be so ashamed. And now here is Hester threatening to
rise to your level, and saying it is her duty, or her destiny
or something puffed up. So tell her what you know
about it, which must be all that is known, and spare her
nothing."

"Well, I know it is my destiny," said Miss Burke.

"Well, tell her how nobly you fulfil it. Tell her what
employers are like without meaning it, or even meaning
it, which is quite unspeakable, though you have the
courage to speak of it. And tell her how hurt Plautus is
by the thought of her leaving him."

Miss Burke was checked by the last suggestion.

"There is nothing heroic in losing the provision that
was made for one," said Hester, in a quiet, controlled
tone, glancing at Miss Burke. "It does make me feel
rather brave to be thrown on the world at forty-nine.
But when courage is called for, what can we do but
have it?"

"Well, what of me, bearing my loneliness with simple
resolution?" said Emma, clasping her hands. "And
what of this dear one, serving others all the days of her
life? It seems quite common to be brave. There is no
need to be eager about it."

"I have not the courage to live on charity any more
than Miss Burke has."

"I have the courage but not the chance," said the
latter. "And I should call it not being above accepting
generosity."

"There, Hester, you can call it that, and accept it for
my sake, and be living for others all the time. And if
you work, you will be living for yourself, and how could

you dream of doing that? It is what I do myself, and I never dare to think of it. The very thought would drag one down, or perhaps make one see how low one is."

"You would not say that Miss Burke lived for herself."

"I should like to," said the latter. "When my mind is not on my work, I daresay I do."

"There, Hester, your mind might not be on your work. And think how dishonest that would be. Do tell her, Miss Burke, as you know about it."

"Do you think Mrs. Hume would engage me?" said Hester. "I need not tell her I have never had a post before."

"I think she might," said Miss Burke. "You are better educated than I am, and of a different class. That is how she would see it. And not to have had other posts, not to have needed to have them, might make her respect you."

"Scheming for respect," said Emma. "It is very lowering, Hester. And I thought she wanted a companion. Or does she really want one?"

"She wants someone who will rise to emergencies," said Miss Burke. "It may be a house where they occur."

"I can do no manner of work," said Hester. "I toil not, neither do I spin——"

"Yes, you can go on," said Emma, looking at her clothes.

"I made the mistake of telling her that I left my last post, because they asked me to wash the dishes," said Miss Burke.

"And you made the mistake of not telling us, dear?"

said Emma, in gentle question. "Because you have been doing it, haven't you? I thought I heard you."

"The better ones; that is a part of companionship," said Miss Burke, smiling. "And I had Plautus to support me."

"Yes, make a mock of us, dear, if it is a help to you."

"And you advertised for a working housekeeper. That was at any rate honest."

"Oh, do we deserve that? Of course we are at our worst when we advertise and state our selfish needs; but it sounds as if we said what we thought, or meant what we said, or something else malicious; and perhaps we did mean it."

Plautus walked to the door and stood in front of it.

"He is asking to be let out," said Hester.

Plautus was doing this, and he meant what he said.

"He ought to learn to open the door himself," said Miss Burke, as she returned from doing so for him.

"He would do it, if his will could help him," said Hester. "He looked as if his eyes would bore through the wood. Oh, he all but opens it."

"But not quite," said Miss Burke, who had all but not done so.

"Oh, Plautus expects to be attended on."

"Then he should have an attendant," said Miss Burke, as if this were not at present the case.

"We ought to have done it, dear," said Emma, "and we meant to in our hearts. You must take the will for the deed with all three of us."

"Mrs. Hume will not do that," said Miss Burke, with some vigour. "She wanted deeds and did not disguise it."

"Does she think that actions speak louder than words? I never know if they do; I always hope not; and they do not often have the chance. But if she does, why does she advertise for a companion? She must know that she runs the risk of companionship."

"I should not advise Miss Wolsey to depend on it. But she may fare better than I did. 'To him that hath shall more be given,' and Mrs. Hume would act accordingly."

"So you are a cynic, dear. I wonder if she knew that. She could not have failed to esteem you."

"She did fail to. And cynicism would not help with washing the dishes."

"Wouldn't it? I don't think I could wash them without it. And I don't think you could either. I am sure you always wash them with it."

"I must pose as a helpless gentlewoman, who has never soiled her hands," said Hester. "I am faced by sudden poverty and resolved to be a burden on no one."

"Why is it a pose?" said Emma.

"Do you think Mrs. Hume will respect that?"

"Not the last part," said Miss Burke. "She would have more respect for burdens."

"Well, so should I," said Emma. "I hope I should have the resolution to be one. It is the sort of courage I admire."

"But not the sort that I do," said Hester.

Plautus gave a yawn.

"Dear one!" said Hester. "He might be a human being."

"There are other things he could have in common with one," said Miss Burke.

"Can your cynicism be natural?" said Emma. "I hardly knew there was such a thing. We have no right to your services. But it will make us value them. Cynicism is never wasted, like effort or pity."

"How did Plautus get back into the room?" said Miss Burke.

"The door is ajar," said Hester. "Did you think he could open it?"

"No," said Miss Burke, who knew he could not. "But it is only ajar about an inch."

"That is enough for Plautus. He can make himself into air. I believe he could get underneath it."

Plautus made himself into air and alighted on Miss Burke's shoulder, and she gave a start and shriek.

"Get away from me, cat, and keep away. I cannot bear the touch of you. And don't expect me to open the door. Get underneath it."

"Oh, don't say more than you mean, dear," said Emma. "And don't call Plautus 'cat'."

Plautus reached the floor without sign of inconvenience, and moved smoothly away.

"They always go to people who do not like them," said Emma, voicing a current belief.

"So they do," said Hester, welcoming Plautus into her lap with every sign of affection.

"He seems determined to settle on someone," said Miss Burke, shuddering as she used the suggestive phrase.

"Now, Hester, you must stay at home to protect

Plautus and Miss Burke from each other. It would be cowardly to leave them undefended."

"Does Mrs. Hume keep a cat?" said Hester. "It would help me to feel at home. I might be just reminded of Plautus."

"I expect she does," said Miss Burke. "She looks as if she would."

"Yes, insult us, dear," said Emma. "It will be an outlet for you. You have had a shock. Plautus is so ashamed. He cannot lift his head or look you in the face."

"I daresay not, as he is going to sleep. It is the best thing he can do."

"Oh, but we do not see the changing expressions on his face," said Hester.

"And he does not see those on ours," said Miss Burke. "Mine would be new to him."

"Oh, I don't think he looks at us," said Hester, as if this exalted Plautus.

"I am sure he does not," said Miss Burke, as if it did not do so.

"It is an impressive thing, a cat's complete self-absorption," said Emma, dreamily. "There is nothing human that compares to it."

"I hope not," said Miss Burke. "We should not like it in each other."

"No, it would lack a cat's aloofness and distance."

"Plautus, did you ask me a question?" said Hester.

"Perhaps silence is consent," said Miss Burke.

"Tell me what you said, Plautus."

Silence did not serve this time, and Hester turned to Emma.

"I must write to Mrs. Hume. I shall not say I have heard about her. I shall simply answer her advertisement. I decided how to describe myself."

"You should ask for an interview. Then she will think you are a woman of the world. You can judge of each other when you meet. That is, you can judge as well as she."

"So I proved I was not one," said Miss Burke. "I let her suggest the interview. That was my first mistake."

"You should not behave like a companion, when you are going to be one. You should assume they could not think of you in that way. If there is any hint of that, Hester, come straight home, and Miss Burke will comfort you, as only she can know how."

"What sort of a family is it?" said Hester.

"Five people beside Mrs. Hume," said Miss Burke. "A husband, a son, and three tall children."

"Do the interviews take place in public?"

"They take place where Mrs. Hume happens to be."

"And she wants a companion!" said Emma. "She must have a passion for companionship. And I think you said she has a cat as well. She must have an over-social nature."

"Yes, Plautus, it is a privilege to put a cushion for you, is it?" said Hester. "And to see you settle on it, as if no thanks were needed?"

"A cat is at once more and less than a human being," said Emma.

"Now why did he ask for a cushion, if he did not want it? What was in his mind?"

"We shall never know. To think we shall never know! You will not tread on him, dear, will you?"

"No, I will not indeed."

"She does not love you enough even to tread on you Plautus," said Hester. "Now I am not going to read my letter aloud. No one can apply for a situation and be at her best, and Plautus likes me to be that. I said I had to earn my living, which was anyhow dignified and honest."

"And still was not your best?" said Emma. "Ought not Mrs. Hume to know that? Though it is never dignified for a woman to say such things. And it is not really honest, when everything I have is yours."

Plautus signified a wish to leave the room, but met with no response.

"If he came in by that crack, he can go out by it," said Miss Burke.

Hester rose in silence and opened the door, and Plautus hastened forward and paused in the doorway.

"There is such a draught," said Emma. "Does he want to go in or out?"

Plautus wished to do neither.

"How he knows his own mind!" said Hester.

"We might take the other view," said Miss Burke.

"You are almost too far above us, dear," said Emma.

"Not above Plautus," said Hester. "He lives in a world apart. He knows things that we do not, all manner of things of his own. I expect he knows the way the stars go round."

"Then he has not paid much attention to the earth," said Miss Burke. "Now, Plautus, this way or that!"

She made a sound with her hands and feet, and Plautus gave a start and a glance and fled.

"How resolute of you, dear!" said Emma. "To do a thing that threw light on you. I should not have had the courage. There will never be any light on me."

"Well, not that sort of courage," said Hester. "Poor Plautus, has he gone away to cry by himself? I must go and comfort him."

She went out with this purpose, but found it was not Plautus who needed comfort. He was sitting on the grass behind the house, with an air of doing something deeply congenial, his eyes on some birds, who were fluttering and crying under his openly sinister scrutiny. It was true that he knew things that they did not, and he was engaged with them at the moment.

Miss Burke turned to Emma.

"Do you think I shall suit you, Miss Greatheart? I have not pretended to be anything but what I am."

"I am sure you have not, dear. And what a question, when you are a family friend! And when you persecute Plautus, as if it were your established privilege, which of course it is. You cannot expect an answer."

"I shall be glad to settle down. I have never felt so much at home on my first day."

"No, I thought perhaps you had not. And we are quite dependent on you. There is no such thing as time. I have not asked you if you can be happy with us. When what we give is food and shelter and a salary, and happiness does not depend on material things, it seems a foolish question."

"You don't know how much worse—how different it is in most places."

"Yes, I do. I think it is more different than it is. We are never as different from other people as we think, or as we ought to be. But I hope Hester will not be able to bear it. I am sure Mrs. Hume is the very person for her. Wanting companions when she has so many! Of course the companion will be put to other purposes."

"Am I to direct the maid? Or do we both take our orders from you?"

"You could both take them from Hester, if she were to be here. But now you will give them all to the maid. You will treat her as you do Plautus, and she will look up to you and be content."

"I shall remember she is a human being. That will be enough."

"Well, dear, if you think it best. You will have to remind yourself of it, if she does not."

Plautus edged round the door, came across the room, and laid a dead bird at Emma's feet.

"Oh, it is too much. Everything he has is mine. Greater love has no one than this, that he lay down his life for his friend. And he knew we could not spare his life; so he found another and laid it down. And perhaps he could not spare it himself. What an element of pathos there is in it!"

"And elements of other things," said Miss Burke. "He is simply a jungle beast."

"Yes, we all prey on each other. The jungle is never dead. It is a strange thought."

"Oh, cruel Plautus!" said Hester, entering. "I did

my best to prevent it. But I was a mere human being and could do nothing."

"And Plautus is a thing apart. His heart beats in tune with the great heart of Nature. And Nature has no pity."

"You are all in the jungle," said Miss Burke.

"No, did you not see Plautus come out of it? He came and laid his all at my feet. What there is in a simple action!"

"Oh, he tried to give it to me at first," said Hester. "But I would not accept it. I cannot countenance everything."

"He gave me no choice. He simply came and told me it was mine."

"He had already told me that."

"He put all his heart into the giving," said Emma, in her dreamy tone. "I could see it in his eye, the complete renunciation."

"Oh, naughty Plautus!" said Hester, shaking her finger. "To catch the bird for me, and think it was a welcome attention."

"You had better share the bird," said Miss Burke. "Plautus will not mind."

"Yes, make us see ourselves through your eyes, dear," said Emma. "You see us through them. We have noticed it."

Plautus carried the bird from the room.

"How clever to solve the problem!" said Hester.

"Poor Plautus, how he wanted it!" said Emma. "Wasn't it pretty to see his lower nature triumphing? So much better than seeing ours doing it. Miss Burke was quite shocked by that."

"He cannot want to eat the bird," said the latter. "He is overfed."

"No, it is sport for its own sake. When we hunt a fox, we do not want to eat it. Perhaps it seems to make it worse. But I believe Plautus did want to eat the bird. He has taken it away to try to do it."

"Have you ever kept a dog?" said Miss Burke, speculating on the result of this.

"Yes, but he could not have been a proper one. When we moved to this house, he did not make his way back on foot to the other. And when someone died, he was never found on the grave. And his behaviour with a bone could only be called grudging. He was on a different level."

"Yes, Plautus does all he is supposed to do," said Hester, "and some things he can't be prevented from doing. Ah, Plautus, come in and tell me if you will think of me when I am gone."

Plautus walked to the fire, giving no sign of doing so while she was there.

"Shall we shut the door?" said Emma. "He seems to be settling down."

"Oh, that is why you keep it open," said Miss Burke.

"Well, we should not want a draught for its own sake," said Hester.

"It seems that the house is run for the cat."

"For Plautus? Well, it belongs to him. We are here as his companions."

"It has been practice for you. You can tell Mrs. Hume you have had experience."

"But she may not know that a cat is human."

"Of course, that is possible," said Miss Burke.

"Dryness is wasted on us, dear," said Emma.

"All that we have is his," said Hester. "Miss Burke will learn to feel the same."

"What I have, would not be much good to him, if he wants things on this scale."

"Oh, Plautus must have an establishment. It is his due."

"Your feeling for him really comes from the maternal instinct," said Miss Burke, driven to this length.

"Well, of course we are frustrated, dear," said Emma, "and the result of over-civilisation; though I hardly think there is such a thing, or there would be other signs of it. But only frustrated people can live for themselves. Fulfilled people seem to live for others. And we are not fitted for that."

"I thought you lived for Plautus."

"Yes, dear, we know what you thought."

"I did not really mean anything."

"No, no, dear, it was the book that meant it. Those books always say a thing is something else, and tell you what it is. And of course it is that, and we know about it; but it is better not to say what we know. There might be some reason for our knowing it. Just as there is for saying it."

CHAPTER IV

"I MUST EXPRESS my regret, Miss Wolsey, that I am here alone to receive you. My parents are obliged to be out, and my young cousins were not deemed equal to the task of making you welcome; I should say to the privilege of doing so."

"It is better to meet like this, when I know none of you. Mrs. Hume took a risk and engaged me without an interview. I am more of a stranger than I might be."

"I believe my mother prides herself on her power to judge people through the post. She says they reveal themselves—I believe her words were 'expose themselves'—unconsciously through that medium. We may deduce that your revelation was a happy one."

"And what the eye does not see, the heart cannot rue," said Hester.

"And what the eye does see," said Rosebery, taking her coat in the manner natural to a matter of course, "the heart may salute, if I am permitted an opinion. And now may I attend to your comfort? At what distance will you be from the fire?"

"This chair seems to strike the mean."

"But it also," said Rosebery, in grave concern, "coincides with the vested rights of my mother. So I will take the choice as an augury of your agreement with her, and ask you to make another. We do not wish her return to be the signal for your displacement. And she herself would not wish it."

"Thank you very much for telling me. It would be a poor beginning to be found in her place."

"It would not be the most auspicious one," said Rosebery, smiling and then altering his tone. "These little sanctities of a household, Miss Wolsey, have a significance beyond themselves and do not invite a breach. I thank you for respecting them. And now I will ring for tea."

"That is a pleasant word. My journey seemed longer than it was."

"These little, cross-country journeys are very tedious," said Rosebery, in serious conviction. "They seem to lack the capacity of winding to their end."

"It is the better to feel at home, when they have done so."

"Miss Wolsey, I trust you will feel that in this house. I was distressed to learn the reason of your coming, and to know that we must see our gain as the result of your loss. But I hope there may be compensations."

"I shall have my share of the gain. It is always something to know fresh people and learn fresh lives. It adds to oneself in the end. One is a larger person."

"That sort of courage will carry you far. I could find it in me to envy you. We are proof against misfortune when we have that within us, that enables us to use it."

"Well, tea is a help in whatever we have to do."

"Miss Wolsey," said Rosebery in a serious tone, "I am going to ask you to pour it out. I think a man never looks so misplaced as when he attempts to preside at the tea table. It is so emphatically the woman's place. And

I propose to safeguard myself against cutting so sorry a figure."

"Well, am I to come to the table or is the table to come to me? The first will involve my taking the sacred seat."

"Mohammed will come to the mountain," said Rosebery, bringing the table forward. "And I admit that in a measure 'sacred' is the word. I speak as a mother's son, and perhaps in a fuller than the usual sense."

"Do you take milk and sugar?"

"Miss Wolsey, I am going to make a confession. I take sugar as a rule, because I have not had the heart to break it to my mother that I have lost my taste for it. She has always indulged me with the generous lumps. I will drink my tea sugarless on this occasion, and find the stolen waters sweet, the more so that they are unsweetened."

"Do you lead a busy life?"

"I am less occupied than I might, and perhaps should be, as a man in the prime of life. I have been much tied to my mother of late, though there is no implication of unwillingness. It is hoped that your presence may enable me to be of more use to my father, who is engaged in the country duties, in which I am his natural assistant, and to which I am his successor. The elder of his nephews will eventually follow me."

"You mean, if you do not marry?" said Hester, after a pause.

"I mean, as I shall not marry," said Rosebery, with grave emphasis. "We are told to know ourselves; and it is permissible to claim that degree of self-knowledge, and to give my account of it."

"Many men have said what you say, and found their mistake."

"Very few men of my age. I am no beardless boy, to change my serious intentions with every month. My account of myself may be taken as the true one."

"Well, you look very comfortable in here," said another voice, as Miranda entered with her husband and niece and nephews, her eyes going rapidly about the room. "How do you do, Miss Wolsey? I am glad you are here safely, and are making yourself at home."

"Your son has helped me to be that. I could hardly have gone so far by myself. And I shall feel more so, now that I meet you all, and begin to be one of you."

"You are very much what I imagined you to be," said Miranda, smiling as she shook hands, and suggesting by her tone that she did not refer only to appearance. "I wonder if you can say the same of me."

"I told Miss Wolsey of your power of divination through the post, Mother. And it may appear that she can claim her share of it."

"Yes, my imagination served me well," said Hester, not mentioning the assistance rendered to it by Miss Burke. "I feel as if I should have known you, perhaps not anywhere, but in any place where you were likely to be."

"I would perhaps not go as far as that. But my picture was not very wrong. Now I must introduce my husband. Julius, you have not met Miss Wolsey. My son has done more than introduce himself. You children can shake hands and then keep out of sight. Now shall we have the tea-table in its proper place? It seems to have taken a leap."

"We moved it, Mother," said Rosebery, in an open tone, "or rather I did so, in order that Miss Wolsey should not be found in occupation of your seat, an encroachment she was anxious to avoid."

"It is you who would have had the seat, and you could have moved when I came in. Oh, did Miss Wolsey pour out the tea?"

"In response to a request from me that she would save me from the situation, which never seems to me to show a man to advantage."

"That is needlessly self-conscious in your own home. And Miss Wolsey need hardly have been troubled with duties so soon."

"Do you not agree with me, Father, that a man officiating at the tea-table is a signal example of a person out of place?"

"The tableau was certainly better as it was."

"Did you see it, as you came in?" said his wife.

"I saw it, as it was dispersed."

"There was no need for that. Miss Wolsey could have poured out tea for us all," said Miranda, with a suggestion that this might have been required of her.

"Now, Mother!" said Rosebery. "When your first request was for the table to be restored to its place!"

"It may as well be put to its use, now it is there," said Julius.

"Well, shall we pursue the sugar basin?" said his wife. "I do not know how it got on to that table by itself. The things seem to have taken on a life of their own. And you must have had your tea without sugar, Rosebery."

"Well, I will have another cup with it, when other people have been supplied."

"Can I give you another cup, Miss Wolsey?"

"No, thank you. I have had more than one."

"Ring the bell, Adrian," said Miranda, looking into the teapot. "There is not enough tea here for us all. You must have had several cups too, my son."

"I suggest, Mother, that the pot was supplied for two people, and that the onslaught of the rest of you has upset the balance."

"There is no question of onslaught, with the pot in this state. Some fresh tea, Bates, and some more hot water. Was this tea made for two people, or was it meant to supply us all, as usual?"

"The latter I think, ma'am. I was present when Cook measured it. And she made no comment."

"Well, it is better to be over than under-hospitable, Rosebery. Bring up your chair, Miss Wolsey, so that we can talk. Well, well, my son, that little effort hardly needed your help. Bring up your chair as well, into its place by mine. You shall soon have a cup of tea to your taste."

"I hardly think I need any more, Mother. It seems I have already exceeded a normal allowance."

"It does not matter whether one or both of you has done so. It is too small a point to pursue."

"I suggest it was myself, Mother. I was protesting my inability to deal with the tea, and dealing with it in another way all the time," said Rosebery, ending with a laugh.

"Oh, here is a beautiful sight!" said Hester, stooping

to caress a cat, that had accompanied Bates into the room. "Here is someone who makes me feel at home. He does just remind me of an important personage there."

"So you have a cherished cat, Miss Wolsey?" said Julius feeling a word from him was due.

"I have a friend who happens to be a cat," said Hester, looking into his face. "He was very upset by my leaving him. He had not given me permission."

"No cat would be disturbed by a thing like that," said Miranda. "How did this cat get into the drawing-room, Bates?"

"He followed me along the passage, ma'am. I had omitted to shut the door. He is always on the watch for an oversight."

"What is his name?" said Hester.

"I am not quite sure," said Miranda. "Has it a name, Bates?"

"We call him Tabbikin, ma'am."

"But he is not a tabby," said Hester.

"The name was suggestive of a cat, ma'am."

"Is it a good mouser?" said Miranda.

"I believe Cook is satisfied, ma'am."

"Oh, Tabbikin, fancy your being kept for your baser qualities! What would you say to the life my Plautus leads?"

Tabbikin went towards the fire, looked round to see if his presence would be tolerated, and turned and withdrew, as though disinclined for risk.

"Is he happy in the kitchen?" said Hester.

"I expect it is well cared for," said Miranda. "It is there to be of use."

"Does he eat the mice when he catches them?"

"No, it is too well fed. Unless that was our last cat."

"He plays with them for a time, ma'am. He only infrequently eats them. He sometimes brings them to Cook."

"Oh, my cat brought a bird to me the other day," said Hester, simplifying the truth unconsciously. "It is sad that they have these propensities."

"I fear, Miss Wolsey, that to my mother they are the justification for their existence," said Rosebery, smiling.

"Oh, fancy keeping a cat for what he can do for you, and not for what he is! A cat's only obligation is to be himself."

"A cat would never be anything else," said Miranda. "We take advantage of its instincts."

"We do not do that with Plautus. We like him to suppress them."

"Perhaps our cat is really the more fortunate," said Julius.

"But how much less fortunate you are yourselves!"

"You had a roundabout journey, Miss Wolsey, and a halting train."

"Yes, I found myself feeling inclined to get out and walk."

"That would not have helped you," said Miranda. "What kind of household did you leave?"

"My friend with whom I share a home, our house-keeper and the cat. All of them equally important in their way."

"Will your friend be able to keep up the house by herself?"

"She always bore the larger part of the expenses," said Hester, keeping her eyes from Julius and speaking with open simplicity. "She was better off than I was. But now I can contribute so little that I should be in effect dependent on her. And that I could not be."

"You are very wise. A plan like that could only have one end."

"I do not see why, Mother," said Rosebery. "Why should not Miss Wolsey make her contribution in the form of her presence?"

"If you need me to tell you, you have less knowledge of life than you should have at your age."

"I daresay that is so. Knowledge of life has never been one of my ambitions. It seems to imply an acquaintance with things of which it is as well to be ignorant."

"Why should it not include all things?" said Julius.

"That is not called knowledge of life, Uncle," said Francis.

"Let us talk about the things that are called that," said Alice.

"I told you to keep in the background," said their aunt.

"But the lure is too strong for us," said Francis. "We did not know that Miss Wolsey's affairs would hold such promise."

"It seems too good to be true in a companion," said Hester, smiling.

"Miss Wolsey's affairs are nothing to do with you," said Miranda.

"Surely, Mother, that is hardly the case, now that she

is a member of our household," said Rosebery. "They are a natural matter of interest to us all."

"Well, go on probing into them. But I don't know what she will think of you."

"Mother, it was you who asked the leading questions."

"Ask me anything you like," said Hester. "I have no dark secrets. My life is a simple, open thing."

"Is your friend upset by your leaving her?" said Alice.

"Yes, I am afraid she is."

"Then is she willing to support you?" said Adrian.

"Yes, that is what she wished to do."

"Miss Wolsey, it is a great tribute to you," said Rosebery.

"She might not continue in that mind," said Miranda. "It is a thing it would be easy to get tired of."

"Mother, the cynical touch is sure to come from you."

"You can cultivate simplicity too far. There is no cynicism involved in an experience of human nature."

"It is perhaps the second that produces the first," said Julius.

"Well, Father, that is cynical."

"Ah, Tabbikin, what do you think of it all? Are you a cynic or not?" said Hester, stooping and extending her hand.

"The cat is not here," said Miranda. "You will not entice it out of its place, Miss Wolsey? We do not want it with us."

"I may speak to him if I see him? I don't think I could pass him without a word."

"I hardly think she could, when she cannot be apart from him without one," said Alice to her brothers.

"He would pass you without a look," said Julius.

"Well, why should he not? I am not nearly so worth looking at. His personality is so much more appealing than a human being's."

"Do you really think a cat is more interesting than you are?" said Miranda.

"Oh, but yes. How can I compete with him in grace and charm?" said Hester, putting her hands together and just looking at the men. "And his dependence on himself, when I have always leant on other people! There is no comparison."

"It is more sensible not to make one. We cannot impute human qualities to a beast. And a cat is a selfish creature."

"Surely selfishness is a human quality."

"Less marked in human beings than in cats."

"Ah, Tabbikin," said Hester, again extending a hand, "so you are more selfish than we are? Now can that be true?"

There was a pause.

"Miss Wolsey is so used to being with a cat, that she cannot accept any other conditions," said Julius.

"And how can I be expected to?" said Hester, meeting his eyes. "Not have a cat to compensate for human awkwardness! What a waste of opportunity!"

"No one here is awkward," said Miranda, "unless imputing the quality deserves the name. Yes, I shall talk in my own way, Julius. My age and my position place me apart. No one can be with me, who does not accept it."

"And we are all with her, Miss Wolsey," said Rosebery. "So you must gather what you may."

"Well, I do not want you with me any longer. I wish to have an hour with Miss Wolsey alone. She did not undertake to be a general companion. And she will be more at her ease when you are all gone. She is used to being with women. You can go and help your father, my son. My having a companion was to set you free, and it can begin to do so. Now Miss Wolsey, draw up your chair and we will have a talk. Would you like some more fresh tea? Or would it be too much to have it a third time?"

"Yes, it would indeed. But it was good to have it twice, after a tedious journey."

"The journey could only have taken an hour or two."

"But it should only have taken twenty minutes. And the discrepancy gave the impression of tediousness. Ah, Tabbikin——" Hester straightened herself and looked aside.

"You can forget the cat. You will soon get used to being without one. And I daresay it will do you good. Now, settle down and be at your ease. It is not being so that makes you behave unnaturally. You are not used to men, and they make you aware of yourself. But you will not have much to do with them."

"No, I am here to be with you," said Hester, her look of open-eyed perplexity fading at the last words. "And I hope I shall be that constantly. It is the reason of my coming."

"I am sorry you have lost your income," said Miranda, in a sincere tone. "But I am fortunate to have someone who has had one, and so had what goes with it.

It will mean that we can associate on equal terms. It will make a better companionship."

"If it was not on equal terms, it would not be one, would it?"

"Well, well, these things are as they have to be. And, while I think of it, will you show as much knowledge and experience as you can, when you talk to me, and not as little? I have no use for simplicity, assumed or otherwise. And when it is the first, nothing can be done for it."

"I shall get to know just how far you like to go," said Hester, in a cordial tone. "And of course I will adapt my standard to yours. It is only my duty."

"You will have to do the best you can with my standard," said Miranda, smiling. "And as we are talking in this way, there is something I should tell you. My son is a confirmed bachelor, and has nothing to give to any woman but his mother. It is due to any single woman, who is to be thrown with him, to explain that. You do not misunderstand me?"

"No, it is quite simple, isn't it?" said Hester, again with the perplexed look. "You only mean what you say. I am to know that your son has nothing to give me. And that is only fair, if things should be the same on both sides."

"Well, you have nothing to give each other. So you will remember it, and he will not need to do so. It was right to warn you, as you are unaccustomed to men, and your instincts may be stronger than you realise."

"I daresay they are," said Hester, in a rueful manner. "They are bound up in the home I have left. I suppose the home instinct is strong in any woman. And they say that my maternal instinct is expended on Plautus; and that may have its element of truth. And my instinct for human affection is fulfilled by my friend. So my instincts are fully occupied."

"Your deepest instinct is not. But we need not go into that. You understand my warning. You would not be the person you are, if you did not. So we can pass to other subjects. Is your money irrevocably gone? I sympathise deeply with you about that."

"It was in a single security that has ceased to pay. 'Security' seems an ironic term. And I am afraid my instinct of possession is stronger than I knew. It surprises me how much I mind."

"It is surely natural to mind. Is there any hope that the investment will recover?"

"I cherish the hope, and imagine myself restored to my home and my friend and my cat, with all my instincts satisfied. As it is, it is little wonder that they fix themselves upon Tabbikin."

"Is your cat a very well-bred animal?" said Miranda.

"Oh, I do not know. He is not an animal to me. He is a complex and subtle personality. I hardly find any other more interesting."

"You will learn to do so. I think you are already learning. Your life has not helped you to know men or women or yourself."

"I think, if we did not do the last instinctively, we should never do it. There is another instinct with a duty to fulfil."

"Some of us are misled by our conception of ourselves.

That is quite another thing. But we will not run these matters to their death. You would like to unpack and settle down. The housemaid will show you your room and give you any help you need, though perhaps you would hardly be dependent on it. We shall be having dinner in an hour."

"I am indeed not dependent on it. That would not fit at all with my conception of myself. Not that it is a thing I ever think about. Do you think about yours?"

"I would recommend everyone to do so sometimes. It may need to be brought up to date. But you need not keep using my words again. You have enough of your own."

"Well, I will go and unpack, while you bring yours up to the last minute," said Hester, as if she did not hear the last words. "And I will leave mine alone, as is my habit."

Miranda smiled to herself and took up the paper. She discussed public matters with her husband on equal terms. When the latter came in, he broached a personal one.

"Where is Miss Wolsey?"

"She has gone to her room. I do not keep her on a lead. You need not ask where she is, whenever you do not see her."

"I wondered what had happened to her."

"Why, what should happen?"

"Your talk might have been too much for her."

"It was as much as she liked, but no more than she needed. I think she saw that, though she pretended not to. She did her part rather well. She is not a stupid woman."

"What did you have to say to her?"

"Really only one thing. But it took its own kind of saying."

"You mean it was a thing that really could not be said?"

"By many people perhaps. There is nothing I cannot say."

"That is what I was thinking," said her husband.

Rosebery came into the room and looked about him.

"Where is Miss Wolsey, Mother?"

"You can ask your father. I cannot tell everyone who comes in, the same thing."

"She has gone to her room," said Julius.

"Will she be down to dinner?"

"Well, she will not want to miss her meals," said Miranda, just uttering the words. "That is not her object in coming."

The children entered and also looked about them.

" 'Where is Miss Wolsey?' " said their aunt.

"Well, where is she?" said Francis. "Not fled the house so soon?"

"Gone to her room," said Rosebery. "A most natural thing to do."

"In a state of collapse?" said his cousin.

"Why, what should be the reason for that?"

"I thought she had had a talk with Aunt Miranda."

"You will have one yourself, if you are not careful," said his aunt.

"Your youth and dependence, Francis, may render

you liable to criticism from which she would be immune."

"She is coming downstairs," said Miranda, in a tone of mild caution.

Hester entered, took in the group, and came towards it.

"I have unpacked and settled down and made myself presentable all in an hour. Have I not done well?"

"Answer her, some of you," said Miranda, wearily. "It is to you she is speaking."

"You flatter us, as you know, Mother," said Rosebery. "But if we are to answer, she has done well indeed, and we congratulate both her and ourselves on the result."

"Go on talking to her," said his mother, with her hand to her head. "And let her talk to you. Who would want to attend to anyone as old and tired as I am? She does not."

"It is just what I do want to do," said Hester. "I find it a most interesting duty. There is great charm for me in experience; and I understand its natural impatience with those who have had less of it. And I have suspected the tiredness all along."

"It did not account for what I said to you," said Miranda, on a warning note. "That stands as it did. It was necessary to say it, and no one could do it for me."

"It is fortunate that the duty did not fall on anyone else," murmured Francis.

"Is it?" said his sister. "Then it would not have been done. And now nothing can undo it."

"It has been a long day," said Miranda. "It seemed

to start again at tea-time. I do not pretend I am not tired out. I am not in the habit of pretending."

"A statement no one would dispute, Mother," said Rosebery.

"I fear you have had proof of it, Miss Wolsey," said Julius.

"Oh, we most of us give proof of what we are."

"When the obvious course would be to disguise it."

"Dinner is served, ma'am," said Bates.

Miranda rose and walked from the room, and Hester looked round and then followed her.

"What have we before us?" said Francis.

"Whatever it is, Francis," said Rosebery, glancing back, "you will remember that my mother is what she said herself, old and tired; and you will behave to her as a nephew who is indebted to her, would properly behave."

"It is a hard thing to be indebted to anyone."

"Wouldn't it be worse not to be?" said Adrian.

"I am glad you realise it, Adrian," said Rosebery.

"Why are they all downstairs, Bates?" said Miranda. "Is there no schoolroom meal to-night?"

"The sweep has been, ma'am."

"What is that to do with it?"

"It is how Cook expressed it, ma'am."

"Well, you will all three sit in silence. I cannot brook forwardness to-night. And you talk to your father, Rosebery. I cannot take any part. Sit down, Miss Wolsey; no, not by me; there, between the men. I am not equal to talking to a stranger, and as yet you are only that."

"You have found her equal to it, Miss Wolsey," said Julius.

"Oh, I understood. I am not an unperceptive person, and I am here to understand. And although I am interested in experience, I can realise the burden of it. The interest would not be real, if I could not." Hester lowered her tone and sent a swift smile into Julius's face. "And I know I am another woman where there has been only one. And I shall know what it explains. It may take another woman to do so."

"Another woman is what we have needed. My wife has seen it herself. The suggestion was her own. The evil days have come for her, and so for my son and me. It should be for us to help her, but she chose another kind of help. And I am glad of any kind."

"I think I shall be able to give it. I shall know when the words are to be accepted, and when forgotten. It is my sex that is the trouble. I would alter it, if I could. But it will soon become a matter of course. A woman is not an uncommon thing."

"A circumstance for which we all have to be grateful," said Rosebery.

"What circumstance is that?" said Miranda.

"That women are not uncommon, Mother. If they were, we should be sadly placed."

"They are supposed to be too common in this country," said Hester. "We hear about superfluous women."

"Miss Wolsey, it is those we can depend on in our need."

"Is your friend a superfluous woman, Miss Wolsey?"

said Miranda, with her head again on her hand. "I mean, is she also unmarried?"

"Mother! You should say what you mean," said Rosebery.

"She did explain it," said Alice.

"Yes, she is unmarried," said Hester, smiling with the rest. "That is why our friendship is a good one. There is no better kind than that between two single women."

"Miss Wolsey, I can believe it to be so," said Rosebery. "Indeed we have all observed cases of it."

"Have we?" said Miranda. "I had not. But I have not thought much about single women."

"Well, Mother, you will think about one now. You will want her to think about you."

"The cases are not parallel."

"They are not indeed," said Hester. "The thinking is my province, and I have been doing it. I hope you will come with me one day, Mrs. Hume, and see my home and my friend, and yes, I must say it, my cat. It would be a pleasure to all of us."

"I should like to come," said Miranda, in a different tone. "I should enjoy seeing your background, and it would help me to know you better. You are seeing mine, and it would put us on equal terms."

"Miss Wolsey, you are much to be congratulated," said Rosebery, in a low tone.

"Mr. Pettigrew!" said Bates at the door.

"Mrs. Hume, I hope you will excuse this untimely entrance. I came to have a word with my pupils, assuming I should find them upstairs, and was shown in before

I could demur. I had no idea I should intrude upon your evening meal."

"Sit down and share it with us," said Julius.

"Thank you, Mr. Hume, but even did my sense of intrusion permit it, I should have to hasten to the corresponding meal in my own house."

"He is estimating the degree of correspondence," murmured Alice, as Mr. Pettigrew glanced about the board.

Miranda gave a little laugh.

"You have not met Miss Wolsey," said Julius.

"No, I have not, Mr. Hume. But I assume her to be the lady, who I understood was to join your household. And I can assure her there is none more considerate to those who are professionally engaged in it."

"My duties hardly deserve that name," said Hester.

"Miss Wolsey," said Rosebery in a low tone, "they deserve another indeed."

"Let me persuade you to try our fruit," said Julius. "We can buy much better, but we take a pride in our own."

"Indeed, Mr. Hume, I see no difference between that on your table and on mine. And the pride of production is wanting in my case."

"Will you take your wife these grapes?" said Miranda. "We should like her to have them."

"It is most kind of you, Mrs. Hume, and I will act as bearer willingly. Such fruit is beyond our somewhat modest standard, and I am glad for her to have the benefit of it."

"Bates will pack them for you, and they should be easy to carry."

"I have not the least objection to the office. Such sensitiveness would rather deserve the name of self-consciousness. And I shall be supported by the thought of their reception."

"One of the boys can go with you and take them," said Julius.

"I will trouble no one, Mr. Hume. My point of view is as I have stated it, and my actions should not be inconsistent with it. And I trust that no one will leave the table to see me to the door. The maid who brings the parcel will incidentally do so, and it is a needless attention."

"I am going to the village in the morning," said Hester. "Can I leave the grapes on Mrs. Pettigrew?"

"No, indeed, Miss Wolsey, I would not encumber you further than your duty will have done. I would by no means add to your burdens to walk empty-handed myself. Indeed, were I to meet you, I should be happy to relieve you of some of them."

"I would relieve her of all of them," said Francis, as the door closed.

"And I would go with her to prevent her carrying them at all," said Rosebery. "Indeed I suggest that I should do so."

"I do not know what she will be carrying," said Miranda, "unless it is her purse and her umbrella."

"And convention allows me to carry those myself," said Hester.

"How do you manage your house, Miss Wolsey? Are you and your friend domesticated?"

"We have someone to do the managing and cooking,

and a housemaid who does the rest. We are not domesticated; we live simply to avoid being so."

"Miss Wolsey, it must be a great wrench for you," said Rosebery; "to leave the little home that is the harbourer of all your interests, for a house full of strange people, and things unfamiliar and possibly redundant to you. It must need great courage."

"Things are not redundant because they are not essential," said Miranda. "I daresay Miss Wolsey will enjoy them, though she is fortunate to be used to as much as she is."

"Why?" said Julius. "It is surely a natural thing."

"The majority of people have less."

"And I belong to them now," said Hester, "in the sense that I could not afford so much by myself."

"Miss Wolsey, you face it in an ideal spirit," said Rosebery.

"I ought to emulate her," said Francis. "I go on shutting my eyes to my prospects."

"And opening your mouth about them," said his aunt.

"He will always have me behind him," said Julius.

"Of course he will not," said Miranda. "You are fifty odd years older than he is."

"You know what I mean. I am responsible for his future."

"Your money should go to your son. It will barely enable him to fill your place. His cousins will have it in due course."

"Miss Wolsey, you will forgive this broaching of family questions in your presence," said Rosebery. "We

treat you as one of ourselves. Mother, I have no criticism to make of my father's dispositions. My faith in
him is absolute."

"And mine in you in another way," said Julius. "You
will not grudge your cousins their portions. They will
not compare to yours."

"Miss Wolsey, does it strike you as a rare thing for
there to be complete confidence between father and
son? Between a mother and a son it is an accepted
thing."

"Yes, I think perhaps it does, though I had not
thought about it."

"You have not met many fathers and sons," said
Miranda.

"Perhaps not many fathers. I suppose all the men I
have known, have been sons."

"Miss Wolsey, that is so," said Rosebery, laughing.

"But there have not been many," said Miranda.

"Mother, you are getting tired. You will be ceasing
to be yourself. And you were being so much so. I will
take you to the drawing-room and remain with you."

"And leave Miss Wolsey here, so that you and I can
be alone, and she can be where she likes to be, and
where she feels the others like to have her."

"You are killing many birds with one stone indeed,"
said Rosebery, as he followed.

"Are you proof against insult, Miss Wolsey?" said
Francis. "Because, if not, this is no place for you."

"Can you steel yourself to face it?" said Alice. "We
ask nothing that we cannot do ourselves."

"Yes, that kind of insult, the natural antagonism of

a woman in old age to one in her prime," said Hester, speaking easily and not looking at Julius. "I may come to it myself, though it is hard to think it. Ah, Tabbikin, it is no imagination this time. Here you are, all proud and confident in the flesh!"

She intercepted Tabbikin in a furtive approach to the hearth.

"Is there a good fire in here?" said Rosebery, at the door. "The one in the drawing-room has gone out. Miss Wolsey, my mother is coming. What about the cat?"

Hester relinquished it, and the children appeared to be pursuing it, and Julius to be furthering their effort.

"That cat!" said Miranda. "We shall have to get rid of it. Have you been petting it, Miss Wolsey?"

"It occurs to me, Mother," said Rosebery, "that it detects the scent of Miss Wolsey's cat in her dress."

"Oh, that is not a dress she would wear at home," said Miranda, glancing at it.

There was a pause.

"It is not," said Hester, "or rather it was not. It has been handed down to save the expense of a new one."

"So you dress in the evenings at home?"

"We put on something simple, and it sometimes gets replaced by something less simple but shabby."

"That dress is not shabby," said Miranda.

"No, the occasions for it have been few and far between. I wore it so seldom that I let it fill the breach."

"Well, that is sensible enough. You would not have any other use for it."

"Mother, you assume too much knowledge of Miss Wolsey's affairs."

"An ordinary knowledge of things comprises them."

"I wonder if they are kind to him in the kitchen," said Hester, as if to herself.

"Oh, those people always treat an animal as a human being," said Miranda.

"Miss Wolsey, you do not misunderstand my mother?'

"He means the opposite," murmured Alice.

"Oh, I plead guilty to being one of those people myself," said Hester. "I would not be anything else."

"Miss Wolsey, there was no implication intended."

"Do not be foolish, my son," said Miranda. "Do you wonder why we are such close friends, Miss Wolsey?"

"I see there must be things between you, that I do not understand."

"There are things between us, that we ourselves do not understand," said Rosebery. "And we hardly wish to do so. It would be to deprive them of something that goes deeper than understanding."

"The fire has burnt up in the drawing-room, ma'am," said Bates.

"Then we will go," said Miranda. "Oh, there is that cat again. Cannot you keep it in the kitchen?"

"He creeps out when I open the door, ma'am. And he ignores remonstrance."

"He chooses to pass it over," said Hester. "He does not heed human prejudice."

Tabbikin, feeling there was less of this than usual, gained Miranda's knee and settled down with audible purring.

"Why, what a thing to do!" said the latter, looking almost flattered.

"It does not heed human prejudice indeed," said Julius.

"Oh, he surely overcomes it," said Hester. "What a picture he makes!"

"So does Aunt Miranda," said Francis.

"Now, Tabbikin, I do not want you," said Miranda, with a mild effort at displacing him.

He took it for an adjustment for his comfort, and renewed his acknowledgement.

"How it takes to you, Mother!" said Rosebery.

"I have given it no reason to," said Miranda, as though the explanation must lie deeper. "Come, relieve me of it, and let us go to the drawing-room."

Tabbikin followed, crept halfway across the room, cast a look at Miranda and vanished.

"He recognises forbidden ground," said Hester. "No ground is forbidden to Plautus."

"We seem to talk of nothing but cats," said Miranda. "You have certainly imposed your interests—your interest on us, Miss Wolsey."

"I hope I have. It will bring its own reward."

"I am going to bed. I am very tired to-night. Somehow the conversation has exhausted me. Would you come and read to me for twenty minutes? Not talk; read."

"Yes, indeed I will. I am fond of reading aloud. I think it often gives more pleasure to the reader than to the listener."

"I do not want you to read as if it gave you pleasure," said Miranda, in a peevish tone. "It is my pleasure that is my object. And I cannot bear people to read in their

own way. I never like them to show off themselves. I
just want to have the impression of the print. That is
what I am concerned with."

"Mother," said Rosebery, with a note of reproach,
"have you forgotten that reading you to sleep is my
vested privilege? I was not proposing to relinquish it."

"Then come up in half-an-hour. And Miss Wolsey
can stay where she is. That will suit her better."

"That may be true of you to-night, Miss Wolsey,"
said Julius. "You must be tired yourself."

"Miss Wolsey, you did not misunderstand my usurp-
ing what may seem to you your place? My point of view
was as I expressed it. The privilege, or what I regard as
such, is mine."

"I do not grudge it to you. I feel I have been spared a
risk. I could not hold my personality so much in abey-
ance. It is far too definite and wayward a thing. My
impression of the book would somehow make its way
through."

"We have been grateful to you several times this evening," said Julius.

"I have done my best," said Hester, meeting his eyes.
"And I will continue to do it. I am not a person who
turns back."

"You will find my wife's bark is worse than her bite."

"Always an ominous description," said Francis.

"It is the feeling of the power to bite that causes the
bark," said Alice. "And there does not seem much
difference between them."

"People ought not to be allowed to do either," said
Adrian.

CHAPTER V

"Yes, dear, we have to prepare for Hester's visit. Perhaps it makes it worth while to have been without her. I am sure it ought to be a thing like that."

"I wish she was coming by herself," said Miss Burke. "Mrs. Hume does not know I told her of the post, and she may remember me. Had I better keep out of sight?"

"Oh, no, dear, I could not bear not to show you. You are a cause for pride, and I have so few; I cannot think of another. I am so fortunate to have you, and people do admire good fortune. I never lift a finger for myself, and they respect you so for that. And if you keep away, I may have to lift one; and they will think I always do; and that would be most unfair."

"Yes," said Miss Burke, in agreement. "But what shall we say to Mrs. Hume?"

"That Hester had written her letter before you came to us. That is nearly true, as you told us about her so soon. And truth is stranger than fiction."

"That kind of truth is. But Mrs. Hume may only believe the other kind."

"So she may. It is the kind I believe myself. But she cannot say so, and it is voicing things that makes them real. We can feel that about what we tell her."

"I should not be surprised if she could say so. It is the sort of thing she would do."

"Do you suppose she says things to Hester? After all, Hester is her companion, and nothing would make a person so companionable as having things said. I suppose that is the essence of companionship.''

"Well, of that kind," said Miss Burke.

"I cannot bear to think of a demand being made on Hester's courage. There is a subtle unpleasantness in thinking one's friends are heroic. And I am not quite sure it is subtle.''

"What kind of luncheon shall we give to Mrs. Hume?''

"The kind to make her esteem Hester. No luxury and no contrivance.''

"Everything good and plentiful and in season.''

"How you understand me! Almost better than you need. I suppose I had a simple thought. And I hoped I never did. But perhaps it was not very simple.''

"Get out of my way, Plautus," said Miss Burke. "I believe you know we are talking about food.''

"I wonder how he knows that Hester is coming home,'' said Emma, resting her eyes on him.

"Does he know?'' said Miss Burke.

"Yes, there is something different about him, something expectant.''

"Here you are then, Plautus," said Miss Burke, responding to the latter feeling.

Plautus took her offering and moved away.

"Oh, say 'thank you'," said Emma. "Yes, dear, give me a glance of contempt. Expecting Hester has brought back the ways you have cured me of. And I do not want her to find me quite a stranger. I should not dare to let her find it.''

"Do we use the same china as usual?''

"I am ashamed to say we use a better one. We make a difference for guests, which of course stamps us. And we behave as if we did not, which stamps us further. It shows we do things we are ashamed of. But then I think we ought to be ashamed."

"You don't make as much difference as many people."

"How you have seen the seamy side of life! That sort of thing ought to be kept from us. It is not as if we could not think of it for ourselves."

"Well, why should you not be like other people?"

"I think I will tell you, dear. Because I am not like them. And if too much sameness creeps in, I shall be so. And it seems to be creeping in."

"Our ordinary china is cracked and mended. But it is old and good. I should think it is rather rare."

"Oh, then we will use it. Cracked and mended, but rather rare! That strikes the exact note. It is like fine old linen carefully darned. I suppose we have not any linen like that?"

"No, our table-cloths are new and ordinary."

"Not so new that we might have bought one on purpose?"

"No, they have been washed. And people would not do that."

"So they do stop somewhere. How I respect them! And how I ought! I would have bought one, if it had been necessary. And I will tell the truth; I could have had it washed."

"You would not have thought of doing either."

"Thank you so much. I believe that is only just."

"I do not mind belonging to the multitude," said Miss Burke.

"It is a brave lie. And of course you do not belong to it."

"Do you have wine for luncheon when you have guests?"

"Yes, dear, I know I belong to it. There is some in the cellar, kept for these occasions. And we use the napkins that are not mended. As they are not fine linen, there is no harm in that."

"Who mended the others?" said Miss Burke.

"You did, dear. I mean, you could not help not being here."

"I shall not have time for mending. Did the last housekeeper have it?"

"I think she said she made it, dear."

"It is not a thing I can make."

"Plautus, will you mend the napkins?" said Emma, leaning forward. "Forgive me; it is because I cannot meet your eyes. I was afraid I might read your thought."

"I cannot imagine you mending."

"I am so glad. So I might have read it."

"When the napkins want mending, we must discard them."

"I knew you would never be at a loss. Can we hint to Mrs. Hume that we do that? Would it exalt Hester in her eyes?"

"No, I hardly think she would admire it."

"So she does not belong to the multitude. Had we better use the mended napkins?"

"No, they are too much mended. The housekeeper must have made a lot of time."

"Well, she did not keep any for herself. She told us so, when she left."

"Yes, the maid has talked about her."

"How do you know, when of course you do not listen? But you need not be troubled. You shall keep all the time you make."

"I can make many other things better."

"That is as well, because you may have to make them. We shall be five at the table. Mrs. Hume is bringing her son."

"You did not tell me that."

"No, I thought it would give you too much trouble."

"But I had to know in the end."

"That was it. I wanted to spare you the knowledge. So I did as long as I could."

"The son is an odd man. He walked with me to the station. I think he is one of those men who respect womanhood."

"That may seem odd to us, when we know about it. Of course women respect it, but they are the gallant sex. And they are women themselves, and women take personal views of things. But perhaps that is gallant. I think it is."

"And do men respect manhood?" said Miss Burke.

"I think they are known not to be able to. It must be a man's simplicity. I am sure women would respect it; indeed I think they do. They seem to respect both. It really is gallant."

"Will the wine do for the son?"

"Yes, if he is as odd as you say."

"But suppose he is not? I know nothing about him, except that he is attached to his mother."

"There is no need to know him any better. That is enough in these days. Well, Plautus, do you want to see the odd man when he comes?"

Plautus gave no sign of the wish, when the occasion came. He cast a glance at the guests, stayed it for a second on Hester, and walked away.

"Oh, how glad he is to see me! His feelings are too deep for him to show them. So he assumes a veil of indifference."

Plautus looked over his shoulder at the sound of the familiar voice.

"I perceive the indifference," said Rosebery, smiling. "What I question, is whether it is a veil."

"This is a very pleasant house," said Miranda. "It is larger than I had imagined it."

"Mother, it must mean much to Miss Wolsey to return to it. I doubt if we realise what the occasion is to her."

"I have only been away from it for three weeks," said Hester.

"And long weeks they must have been to you."

"No, they have passed rather quickly."

"Miss Wolsey, it is both kind and courageous to say so."

"How long have you lived in the house, Miss Greatheart?" said Miranda.

"We took it fifteen years ago."

"Miss Greatheart," said Rosebery, "we can hardly estimate what the break-up must have been."

"How do you do?" said Miranda, as Miss Burke was

presented. "I think I have seen you before. Oh, you came to see me about the place as my companion! What a coincidence to find you here!"

"Mother, it is indeed a coincidence. Your possible companion and your actual one under one roof!"

"What work do you do here?" said Miranda, not taking her eyes from Miss Burke.

"The housekeeping and cooking. I think the companionship is on the other side."

"So you changed your mind about what you were willing to do?"

"Well, I decided to take the place in this house."

"Did you tell Miss Wolsey about me?" said Miranda, transferring her eyes to Hester, as if such information would be more properly sought from her. "Did you hear of me from Miss Burke?"

"She had written to you on the day Miss Burke came to us," said Emma.

"And you let things take their course, Miss Burke," said Miranda. "That was kind and fair of you, and did more than one of us a service."

"Miss Burke, it was indeed kind of you," said Rosebery, in a low tone deep with recollection.

"I must go and see about the luncheon," said Miss Burke. "It will soon be ready."

"Has it been looking after itself?" said Miranda, her question carrying others.

"No, the maid has been watching it," said Emma. "But Miss Burke feels herself responsible."

"You are very comfortable here," said Miranda, with a faint undertone of surprise.

"Mother, the fact is self-evident."

"That is what I implied, my son."

"Ah, Plautus, you have come to speak to me," said Hester. "Do you know there is another cat where I have been?"

Plautus did know, and acted on the knowledge by putting his nose near her skirt and walking away.

"He is taking his revenge for my desertion. How animals use their reason! They prove it all the time."

Plautus proved it by taking in the group at luncheon, passing his owners and taking his stand by the guests, with his eyes hovering between them.

"No, Plautus, you should not ask to be fed," said Emma.

Plautus understood the injunction and deliberately disregarded it.

"Am I allowed to?" said Rosebery, holding a morsel between his finger and thumb.

Plautus rose on his hind legs, took the morsel and sank back, his eyes not losing their alertness.

"Oh, Plautus, you are not as disciplined as Tabbi-kin," said Hester. "You are allowed to be a human being."

"I am fond of tabby cats," said Emma to Miranda. "They remind me of little tigers."

"My cat is not a tabby. The servants named it. I don't remember what it is."

"A tortoiseshell," said Hester.

"Yes, I think its fur is really rather like tortoiseshell."

"The difference between the two households stands exposed," said Rosebery.

"You are a very good cook, Miss Burke," said Miranda. "That is a thing you did not tell me."

"No," said Miss Burke, who had purposely not done so. "I was to come to you as a companion."

"You are wise to use your talents. To cook well is a great one."

"It is not uncommon, and it has to be used three times a day."

"So you dine at night?" said Miranda, as if the words escaped her.

"Mother, you are showing curiosity."

"I am naturally interested in Miss Wolsey's background."

"Mother," said Rosebery, lowering his voice, "it is hers no longer."

"So you do not find our ways very different from yours, Miss Wolsey?"

"No, they are essentially the same. It is our cats who would find the difference."

"I am glad you can keep up your home by yourself," said Miranda to Emma. "Both for your sake and Miss Wolsey's."

"It would have been the last straw, Miss Wolsey," said Rosebery, "to feel you were unsettling your friend."

"I keep it up so that she may return to it at any moment," said Emma.

"Miss Greatheart, it teaches us how to honour her resolution and independence."

"How did you spend your time when you were here, Miss Wolsey?" said Miranda.

"I suppose I wasted a good deal. I spent it in reading

and gardening and being a companion to Emma and
Plautus."

"Well, there is no great demand on you now."

"Mother, that might be taken as an ungrateful speech.
Tangible services may not be the most valuable."

"It does not do to underrate them," said Miranda,
looking with approval at Miss Burke's activities.

"There are supposed to be some leisured people,"
said Emma. "And if no one wasted time, there would
not be any."

"I feel that shaft goes home," said Rosebery. "I,
the only male present, must take my stand among
them."

"You are indispensable," said Miranda.

"And so was Miss Wolsey, Mother."

"This is excellently made. I congratulate you, Miss
Burke. I regard cooking on this level as an accomplishment."

"There is an especial something about these essentially feminine acquirements," said Rosebery. "I think
we hardly estimate the associations they have for us."

"You have never wanted to cultivate this one, Mrs.
Humc?" said Miss Burke.

"If it had served any purpose for me or anyone else, I
would have done so."

"Well, anyone would do it, who had to. But then it is
a duty, not an accomplishment."

"Miss Burke, in your case it is a signal example of
both," said Rosebery, in a less full tone than he used to
the others.

"You have never thought of adopting a niece or

nephew, Miss Greatheart?" said Miranda, looking from the room to the garden.

"No, and for the most ordinary reasons. I don't want my life disturbed, and I like to spend what I have, on myself."

"Well, the choice is yours," said Miranda, not without a note of respect for the exercise of it.

"If one wanted a child, it would be better to marry and have one in the ordinary course," said Hester.

"It might be better," said Miranda. "But we have to do things as we can."

"Mother, that is surely a needless implication."

"What was it?" said Hester, easily. "That we may not have the chance to marry? Or may not take it? Or may recoil from the sacrifices involved?"

"People do not make the last two implications," said Miranda.

"Well, who would want to make them?" said Emma.

"What man or what woman?" agreed Hester, smiling.

"Miss Wolsey, surely no man would avoid them," said Rosebery, earnestly. "If he thinks any woman takes any chance of marrying, he is a coxcomb indeed."

"Well, coxcombry is not a very serious failing."

"A very ridiculous one," said Rosebery, with a look of distaste.

"A man does more for a woman in marriage than a woman for a man," said Miranda.

"Mother, is that your view? Many people would take the opposite one. Would you say that my father had done more for you, than you for him?"

"Yes, I think I should. Though our case is not a usual one. I am twelve years older than he is."

"What difference does that make?"

"Well, chances get fewer with time."

"You do not mean to imply that you had not other chances?"

"No one means to imply that. But it is no good to pursue a matter where we have no proof."

"Mother, would you confess it, if it had been so?" said Rosebery, with a roguish glance.

"I don't know if I should. If I did, I should be unique," said Miranda, not disclaiming this possibility.

"People would hardly have it to confess," said Hester, "if you mean no chances at all."

"More often than would be admitted," said Miranda.

"Now I am not so sure. I have been surprised by the life-stories that have been unfolded to me."

"You might have been less so by the actual lives."

"We may often be surprised by what is unfolded," said Rosebery, going into mirth.

"Now I do not know," said Hester. "I may be a person who invites outpourings, but I find I cannot discredit everything I am told. The very improbability sometimes speaks for its truth."

"You are an ideal confidante," said Miranda. "To most of us probability would speak louder."

"Mother, cold reason can play too large a part in things."

"It does not often do so."

"Plautus is restless," said Hester. "My return has excited him."

Miranda cast a glance at Plautus's recumbent form.

"Oh, you don't know cats, Mrs. Hume. You have no idea how he rests, when his mind is at peace."

Miranda did not claim to have any.

"You have a very pleasant maid," she said, passing to a subject which she did know. "She must be a great help to Miss Burke."

"Yes, that is her work in life," said Emma. "People are fortunate to have one. I wonder if she knows."

"We never realise our privileges until it is too late," said Miss Burke.

"What do you mean, dear? How you frightened me for the moment!"

"Were you imagining yourself without her?" said Hester.

"I almost dared to fear that she was imagining it. And a coward soul is mine."

"That strikes an echo somewhere," said Rosebery. "I do not remember who had the coward soul."

"You should remember who did not have it," said Miss Burke.

There was a pause.

"Miss Greatheart, the miss of your friend must be great," said Rosebery, as though seeking a reason for Miss Burke's position.

"I can feel I have a place in two homes," said Hester. "That cannot be said of many of us."

"Of a good many who earn our living," said Miss Burke.

"But, Miss Burke," said Rosebery, recovering himself and lowering his voice, "I know it is not the case with you. May I trust that this house may prove a home to you?"

"I am settled and contented here."

"Which is a braver speech than many would realise."

"I am glad to see you so happy and valued," said Miranda to Miss Burke. "I wondered about you, after you had gone. This place makes the demands on you, that you can fulfil."

"I suppose I shall spend my life in fulfilling them."

"In a way that is true of all of us."

"In what way? Some people spend their lives in making them."

"You think I am among those?"

"Well, you must know you are. You are fortunate to be so."

"You do not know the problems of my life."

"No, in a life that appears not to have them, they must be hidden."

Miranda looked at Miss Burke, as if she might have served her purpose better than she thought, and sent her eyes from her to Hester.

Plautus hastened to the door, evinced spectacular impatience, and after a variously assisted and impeded exit, vanished.

"Oh, what is he doing?" said Emma. "Leave the door open and listen. If Mrs. Hume does not feel the draught."

"But I am afraid she does," said Hester, partly closing it.

"What a companion you are! Considering your employer before your cat! To think I should see such a change!"

Plautus returned with an uneasy aspect, went to the fire and remained on his feet, with his head thrust forward.

"He has eaten a mouse," said Miss Burke, "or tried to eat one; I don't know which."

Plautus did not leave her ignorant. He abandoned himself to necessity and laid the result at her feet, with a suggestion of rendering her her due.

"He is repaying you for what you give him," said Emma. "How much better he is than we are! We are known to resent kindness, and he rewards it."

"He ate what the could of the mouse," said Miss Burke. "He thought of himself first."

"Well, we say he might be a human being."

Rosebery went into mirth.

"What are we to do with the mouse?" said Miss Burke.

"Can you not throw it away?" said Miranda.

"No, not without touching it," said Miss Burke, as if Miranda might have seen this.

"What about using the tongs?"

"And feel it soft between them?"

"Everyone has to do an unpleasant thing sometimes."

"No one else is offering to do this one."

"It is not everyone's place to do so," said Miranda, not looking at anyone in particular.

"Ring the bell and ask Adela," said Hester.

Miss Burke rang the bell, and Miranda regarded the action without expression.

The maid appeared with a faintly incredulous air.

"Do you want me for anything, ma'am?"

"Only the mouse," said Emma, keeping her eyes from her face. "Nothing else at all, Adela. And only part of it. It is not a whole one. It is on the floor."

"Oh, *I* could not touch it, ma'am," said Adela, suggesting her relation to the rest of mankind. "I could never lay a finger on anything dead. And it is in a mangled state."

"What do you do, when you have to touch meat or fish?"

"Oh, food is different, ma'am. And it comes prepared. Mother never looks at her fish, before it leaves the hands of the fishmonger."

"Get up and deal with it, my son," said Miranda.

"I suggest the use of the shovel," said Rosebery, rising slowly to his feet. "If we insert it in this way under the mouse, it should simplify Adela's task."

"Oh, I could not even look at it, sir," said the latter, not accepting this interpretation of Miranda's words.

"There is another fire-iron," said Emma. "But I forget what it is."

"The poker will not help us, Miss Greatheart," said Rosebery, coldly.

Plautus snatched the mouse from the shovel and took it from the room.

"He has settled the matter," said Hester. "He thought it was only fair. One can see into his mind."

"He would not let Mr. Hume have it," said Emma, seeing further into it. "He did not feel he had earned it as Miss Burke had."

"I do not want to exceed my due in the matter, Miss Greatheart."

"What do you generally do, when he catches a mouse?" said Miranda.

"He seldom does," said Miss Burke. "He catches a bird sometimes, but they are different."

"It occurs to me, Mother," said Rosebery, "to wonder what happens when our cat at home behaves in a similarly cat-like manner."

"Someone would deal with it. I should not expect to be troubled. This is an indulged household."

"Is it?" said Emma. "I am so pleased and proud."

"It is true that Adela is rather spoilt," said Miss Burke.

Miranda met her eyes.

"Well, shall we all go to the other room?" said Emma.

"Miss Greatheart," said Rosebery, "I am grateful for the word, 'all'. So I am not to be condemned to solitary confinement, which is a situation that does not appeal to me."

"I will go and see about the coffee," said Miss Burke. "It will soon be ready."

Rosebery, who had paused for her to precede him, smiled at her and passed on.

"Miss Burke seems to suit you very well, Miss Greatheart," said Miranda.

"Yes, she does indeed. And I suit her as well as I can. No one can really suit a person who serves her."

"I am sure she has nothing to complain of."

"Well, only her life. And she does not complain of that. I have heard her complain about Plautus."

"Does Plautus complain about her?" said Hester, with a touch of anxiety.

"No, not now he has accepted things. He knows he is dependent on her."

"How can a cat complain?" said Miranda.

"Oh, Plautus knows how," said Hester, "and we both of us understand him."

"He is coming in with the coffee," said Rosebery.

"There is no need to pander to us, Mr. Hume," said Emma.

"I mean at the same time as the coffee," said Rosebery, smiling. "I do not credit him with human capacities, though it seems to be the favoured course."

"Oh, I see you are not pandering to us."

"Miss Greatheart, no criticism was intended," said Rosebery, rising and taking the tray from Miss Burke in time to set it on the table.

"This is excellent coffee," said Miranda. "I must congratulate Miss Burke again. Does she have much practice in making it?"

"We have it after luncheon," said Emma, answering the thought; "but not after dinner, now Hester is not at home."

"Do you miss it after dinner, when you are with us, Miss Wolsey?"

"I did at first, but it is better not to be dependent on such things."

"Not on those extra things. There are many on which we are dependent, of course," said Miranda, suggesting the scope of the provision.

"Everything we have, makes work for someone," said

Emma. "People ought to be like Adam and Eve, who
for a long time did not even put on aprons."

Rosebery laughed, controlled himself and looked at
his mother.

"Have I done something without trying?" said Emma.

"You have betrayed a confused knowledge of the
scriptures, Miss Greatheart."

"Oh, I remember now about it. But I know they had
to work after they had them."

"I think you were trying that time, Miss Greatheart,"
said Miranda.

"What I really feel about these Biblical jests," said
Rosebery, keeping his eyes from the company, "is that
we ought to be chary of indulging in them, as the Bible
lends itself so readily to their success."

"So that we gain easy credit," said Emma, "which is
trying for other people."

"Miss Greatheart, you do not misunderstand my
bearing witness? You would think less of me, if I had
failed to do so. Nothing was further from my thoughts
than to belittle your performance."

"A performance is belittling enough in itself."

"You used the wrong word, my son," said Miranda.

"Well, Mother, provide me with the right one."

"I think you mean 'achievement'."

"Then I substitute it willingly."

"These things must depend on our beliefs," said
Hester.

"We will not pursue that line," said Miranda, with a
note of authority. "We either have the same ones, or
we owe respect to other people's."

"Ought we to respect what we feel to be untrue?" said Emma. "Yes, of course we ought, when it is believed by other people and not by us."

"It is surely paying it the truest respect to try to refute it," said Hester. "Nothing else is taking it seriously."

"Miss Wolsey, it sounds very plausible," said Rosebery just shaking his head.

"You are confusing personal opinions with the truth," said Miranda.

"But our own opinions are the truth to us. Well, Plautus, what do you say about it?"

Rosebery looked incredulous and shocked.

"I feel that animals are as much involved in these matters as we are," said Hester. "They will have their share in any future life there is."

"Miss Wolsey, it has not been so revealed to us."

"I cannot conceive of a future life," said Emma, "in the sense in which we mean it."

"Miss Greatheart, I am grieved for you," said Rosebery, speaking as though this verdict was the last she had expected.

"Let us leave these subjects," said Miranda. "It is not the occasion for them."

"Mother, it is always the occasion to be the defenders of our faith."

"Well, you have been so," said Miranda, whose share in her son's beliefs did not give her his feeling for them. "I was admiring your garden, Miss Greatheart. It makes me ashamed of my own. Do you do much in it yourself?"

"As much as will escape the gardener's notice," said Emma, once more answering her thought.

"Well, my son and I will walk round it, and give you and Miss Wolsey an hour to yourselves. You must have a good deal to say to each other."

"How open she is, when she knows what it must be!" said Emma. "Can she be as much worse than she seems, as the rest of us are?"

"Perhaps not. She does not edit herself. She sees no reasons."

"But she lets other people see them. I have not met another case of it. No, pray do not leave us, dear. You are helping us through our first hour of constraint. And we have no secrets from you. Not even that I dislike Mrs. Hume's son. And that would be a secret from anyone else."

"There is nothing against him," said Hester. "And he is always considerate."

"What a sign of being employed! Grateful for consideration! I was waiting for it."

"Well, all things come to those who wait."

"To think what three weeks can do!"

"They have seen me become a self-supporting woman."

"That ought to be a contradiction in terms."

"I wish it was," said Miss Burke.

"Oh, don't threaten me, dear. I have much to contend against."

"Mr. Hume and the children are all I would ask," said Hester. "The son is a creature apart. Even his father does not know what to make of him."

"What do you call him? You call the father 'Mr. Hume'."

"I call him 'Mr. Rosebery', as the tutor does."

"Hester, do you stop nowhere? Copying the tutor! What sort of man is he?"

"An odd little man, precise and conscious and of another kind."

"Then why do you copy him?"

"In this case he offered me an example."

"I am glad I am not in Miss Wolsey's place," said Miss Burke.

"Think of that, Hester, when she would naturally wish to be in anyone else's! Do not listen to me, dear. I am overwrought."

"Mrs. Hume is enjoying her day," said Hester. "I can see she is impressed by your prosperity."

"Well, of course she is, when my friend is her companion. Companions are solitary and penniless. Have you no knowledge of life or literature?"

"There is not much about companions in literature."

"So you have no knowledge of it. And now you will never get any. Or do you have to read aloud? The thought has just struck me."

"It was suggested, but the son was jealous of the privilege. That is what he called it."

"I never understand why she wants a companion. What can she think of my position?"

"She thinks very well of it, except that you are a spinster."

"I never understand why women are proud of being married," said Miss Burke.

"I do," said Emma. "Someone has wanted to spend his life with them. That is surely a cause for pride. And they have the proof of it, that Mrs. Hume would require. You see I have begun to quote her. It is a good thing I am not a companion. I think I have almost become one. What will you do when she dies, Hester?"

"I do not believe in talking about people's death."

"You have to pretend she is immortal, or you would be failing in your trust. But you must know she is not. I believe even she knows it."

"What do I know?" said Miranda, entering with her son, and assuming the subject to be herself.

"That we are not immortal," said Emma. "Some people do not know it."

"They need not do so until they are old. I think it is better that they should not. I have had to face it, and take thought for those who will outlive me."

"I wish I could talk in a broad and selfless way."

Miranda gave her a smile.

"We have had a pleasant hour. We greatly admired the garden. It is planted with an eye to the present and future, which is both wise and rare. I am sorry Miss Wolsey will miss it this year."

"I hope you will come with me to see it sometimes," said Hester.

"Mother," said Rosebery, "I trust we can give Miss Wolsey opportunity to visit her friend and her garden, without the obligation to include us in the enterprise. This occasion will suffice for a happy understanding of her."

"I must not come too often," said Hester. "It is not wise to live two lives."

"Miss Wolsey, may I hope there was not an undernote in that simple speech?"

"Will you have tea in the dining-room?" said Miss Burke. "You will be more comfortable there."

"Miss Greatheart," said Rosebery, addressing his response to his hostess, "I think our dearest and earliest memories are evoked by the words."

"I hope Miss Wolsey will return to this house one day," said Miranda, as they crossed the hall, "much as I sympathise with her desire for independence."

"I do not sympathise with it," said Emma. "I see no cause for pride in earning one's bread. The very word puts it in its place; there could not be a barer term."

"You and I are fortunate in being above the need to do so."

"You see what you are really proud of. Look at your word, 'above'."

"We should see it as a cause for thankfulness."

"Well, thankfulness and pride are not very different. We should not be thankful for anything we were ashamed of. When we belittle our success, it is because we dare not let our pride have its way. And if you are thankful to something for singling you out, of course you are proud; and surely you ought to be."

"We have done nothing to earn our independence."

"And so we are proud indeed."

"Who is to pour out the tea?" said Miss Burke.

"Whose duty is it?" said Miranda, with a smile.

"Hester's, when she is at home," said Emma. "Otherwise it is Miss Burke's."

"I will pour it out," said Hester. "I know the tastes of everyone here."

She showed this knowledge too openly.

"My son takes sugar, Miss Wolsey. I know you would want me to say so."

"I think I will have a change on this occasion, Mother."

"No, have it as you like it, my son. Miss Wolsey would prefer that. She is pouring out the tea to ensure it."

"Mother, I will make a variation in my habits to-day. I am getting beyond the stage of wanting everything sweetened. I remember an enjoyable cup of tea I had on Miss Wolsey's arrival, when it fell to me to welcome her. She gave it to me sugarless, doubtless judging by my age and appearance; and I realised that my tastes were changing, indeed had changed."

"Then why have you not said so?"

"My reasons have been several. The force of habit is strong, and the sight and sound of the sugar dropping into the cup had become dear. Even now I look for the moment when my senses will be struck by it. But my mature palate no longer craves the sweetness that was acceptable to my youth."

"Well, you cannot have sugar put into the tea without its affecting it."

"That is so, Mother. And therefore I have had to make my choice. And I have made it as I have said."

"But how did Miss Wolsey know?"

"I can only think she remembered the occasion I spoke of. She has the memory of the good hostess."

"She was not a hostess then. It is kind of her to think of it. So you have been drinking tea as you dislike it, for all these weeks?"

"Well, let us say as I once liked it."

"I did not know you were so childish."

"They say we are all children to our mothers. So perhaps this is an illustration of it."

"Why did you not tell me, Miss Wolsey?"

"I did not think of it," said Hester, who had done so and thought better of it.

"You need your mother to care for you, my son. I should not have let you drink distasteful tea, if I had known."

"Well, I will depend on you in future, Mother, and feel I am wise to do so."

Plautus jumped on to Rosebery's knee, causing him to start and exclaim.

"My son is not used to animals," said Miranda.

"Hardly to an animal who joins the family at table," said Rosebery, keeping his tone light, and caressing Plautus.

The latter put his face over the edge of the table and regarded the fare without emotion.

"There is nothing he likes but the milk," said Hester.

Plautus reached her side, waited for his supply of this, and gave his being up to it.

"Now does a human creature yield himself so whole-heartedly to anything?" said Emma.

"Hardly to anything to eat, in public," said Rosebery.

"He ought to have his meals in the kitchen," said Miss Burke.

She took up the saucer, and it appeared to lift Plautus's head up with it and draw him in its wake.

"When you have supplied his needs, Miss Burke," said Rosebery, on her return, "what reward does he make you?"

"He relies on me to go on supplying them."

"And that is a reward surely," said Hester. "I am always grateful for it.

"I am not so easily grateful," said Miss Burke.

"I trust that does not imply that you have met small cause for gratitude?" said Rosebery.

"Why should it do so?" said his mother.

"It might suggest that easy gratitude had been expected."

"It does not do to be afraid to be grateful. We all have our reasons for being so."

"Mother, you bade me keep an eye on the time. And I have the *ungrateful* task of saying it is running short."

"Well, our pleasant day must end," said Miranda. "And it has been very pleasant, Miss Wolsey. We thank you indeed for letting us see your home and helping us to know you better. And we are most glad to have met Miss Greatheart, and hope we may welcome her at our own home very soon."

"And there is the other member of the household," said Hester, lifting Plautus and offering his paw.

"Yes, I must not forget the cat. I am sure it is a most fortunate animal," said Miranda, not suspecting that the paw was at her disposal, and gathering her wraps. "Come, my son, we have no time to lose."

She went down the path, swift and upright, but betraying that it cost her an effort to be so. Rosebery followed at once, to leave Hester to her farewells. At the gate he turned in serious recollection to take leave of Miss Burke, an observance no one else had omitted.

"So we see Hester following her employer with quiet dignity," said Emma. "Why is dignity always quiet? Perhaps it is a good thing that it is. And is it ever shown in fortunate circumstances? Perhaps it is not necessary then. I am glad Mrs. Hume has no curiosity unsatisfied. We should always consider a guest. Why do she and her son like each other so much?"

"I wonder if they really do," said Miss Burke.

"I wondered whether to wonder that. But it did not seem to be necessary. Perhaps they like each other too well. But there did not seem any sign of it. Is it possible that they are just a devoted mother and son? Or can't people be that?"

CHAPTER VI

"Yes, I have had a good day, Julius, a day of interest and pleasure; it is true. But I have to see it as the last piece of pleasure I shall have. I am tired and spent after it, and can hardly give you my account. Well, Miss Wolsey has a good home, and a good friend, and everything that goes with them; and, oddly enough, a house-keeper who came about the post as my companion; you may remember her, a nondescript woman whose name was Burke. She seems to have spoken in my favour, a thing I should not have expected. I made a better impression on her than she on me. But I am inclined to alter my opinion. She is more of a person than I thought."

"Well, you could not know she took that view of you. I remember that you could not."

"I think, Father, that she appears a good deal of a person," said Rosebery, entering behind his mother. "I regard it as a signal instance of the magnanimity that may mark the narrow walks of life. We have not the monopoly of such things."

"Did you think we had?"

"I think we are inclined to associate certain qualities with certain conditions. And they may be fostered by them. That is why this example stands by itself."

"It was certainly kind," said Miranda. "But it cost her nothing. We need not make too much of it."

"Mother, surely the less it cost her, the more it speaks for her. We may be in more danger of making too little of it. How many of us, struggling along an uncertain path, would pause to give a thought to our more fortunate fellows by the way? More fortunate; that is the point to mark. The service, though small, should rank high in the account of human merit. I wish it could win recognition."

"Well, you have given it your own, and can do no more. You can turn your thoughts to your mother. I have something to say to you, my son. Come closer to me and hear it. It is not a sad thing in itself or to me, but sad, I fear, to you. It is the sadness we knew was coming nearer. Yes, my days are numbered, Rosebery; not as they must be for the old, but actually for me. My heart has done its work, and can do no more. And I daresay it has done enough. The doctors were plain with me, when they saw I would brook nothing else. They wanted to see you or your father, but I could say my own word. And now I have said it, no more must be asked of me. My life is spent, and I must lean on others at the last."

Miranda's voice broke on a querulous note, but with no undertone of despair. She had had her time, and would see nothing tragic in its close.

The two men came to her side.

"Miranda, my wife, so it has come, what we have seen ahead. I hoped I should overtake it, but it has held its own. For both of us it is the end."

"Not for you. You have further to go, though perhaps not so far. You will have the children. For you it is not the worst. It is for my son that it is that."

"Mother, it is. But I would not have it otherwise. It is the mark of what I have had. Together we have gone our way; together we will go on, even though with a veil between; even though the one be taken and the other left."

"The days will pass," said Miranda, in a quiet tone. "They will not be many or long. The weakness will come and go, and will come for the last time. And everything else will have done the same. Things have gone easily with me; they are to go easily to the end."

"You see it, Miranda. You are one by yourself," said Julius.

"They will go hard with me, Mother. I must say the word of myself. There must still be truth between us."

"We have always leant on you, my wife. We must have your comfort for your leaving us. You must help us with it."

"Some women might do so. I know it has been done. Dying persons have ordered their own deathbeds. But it is not to be so with me. The time is not our own. I shall go without warning, to you or myself. If there is anything to say, it should be said."

"Mother, there has been no secret between us. There is none now. My mind and heart are open to yours. Nothing holds us from each other."

Julius stood with his eyes on his wife, and suddenly spoke in an aloof, almost light tone.

"I can rise to the occasion better than that. I have the orthodox secret. Nothing is wanting to the drama. Miranda, do you guess what it is? It is near to our hearth and home. It would be like you always to have known."

Miranda sent her eyes over his face and waited for his words. He could say them for himself. It was not for her to help him. Rosebery stood with his eyes dilated. Emotions trembled in the air.

"Miranda, I would give much to say what our son has said. Apart from one thing I can say it. But there is the one thing. At a moment like this there must often be. Do you guess what it is?"

"You are eager for me to guess. I am to say the word as well as hear it. Is that a thing to ask of me now? Tell me the plain truth. Surely the words should not be mine. Surely you are not sparing yourself."

"I have wondered if you knew, if you had seen. Some women would have done so."

"Father, tell her at once. She is in suspense, and that must not be. It can be no great thing."

"I wish it was not; I wish I could think of a small one to tell her," said Julius, in a rapid aside. "I wish I had not had this impulse. It was the shock of what she said; I was not prepared. I had thought to spare her this scene. She should have been spared."

"Tell me the truth," said Miranda, her eyes on their faces and her voice shrill. "Talk to me and not to each other. Tell me in a few words. Which of us should be saved?"

"Miranda, the children; you know my feeling for them. You have thought it was too great. It was not; it was the natural feeling. Do I need to say more?"

"You will say the truth and stop trying to make me say it. Say it, or my death will be upon your head."

"Miranda, it was the time when we grew apart, in Rosebery's early manhood. I was thrown on myself; I had to steer my course as I could; you will remember how things were. My life took on a second thread, as the first one went awry. I had a life apart from you, as you had one apart from me. It ended; the children's mother died; it happened very soon. The tidings came

from abroad of my brother's death. I took them into
my home on the ground that they were his. It was an
easy thing to do; everything played into my hands.
They were penniless; my brother had lost what he had;
it made a plausible whole. They were too young to
question or remember. Adrian was an infant and
Francis three. Was it not a natural thing to do? What
else could I have done?"

There was a silence that had its own force. It
seemed that it could not be broken. Then Miranda
spoke in an even tone, seeming to listen to each word
she said.

" 'And all our yesterdays have lighted fools the way
to dusty death.' That is what mine have done for me.
This is what I have, a dead marriage, now to end in
death."

"Miranda, was it so much? It was only part of my
life. And I tried to share it with you."

"You had those children, and you forgot your child
and mine. You had their mother, and you lived with
her, alive and dead. How it lies clear before me!"

"I should not have told you. I shall not forgive
myself."

"You forgave yourself the thing you did. What you
cannot forgive is the telling of it, and perhaps its time.
And you should have waited longer. It would soon
have been too late."

"I felt the truth was between us, that we could not
part with it unsaid."

"You had lived with it unsaid. But I was not to die
with it so. I was to die, having listened to it. And you

have not long to live with me and my knowledge. You chose your time well."

"I wish I had longer, Miranda. It is the wish of my heart."

"You have not; our time is over; we have only the past that we have seen. What am I to say to you, Julius, in my last hour, on the brink of the grave? That I forgive you, my husband. What else can I say? What other word can pass lips so soon to be closed? And I say them fully. But I thank God that I have not dealt with you, as you have with me."

Miranda's voice ended on its hissing note. Her hands shook, and she pressed them on the arms of her chair. Her breath came shallow and rapid, and as her son approached, she suddenly threw up her arms, turned eyes on him with no sight in them, gave a long, deep sigh and was silent.

"Father, she is dead! She is gone from me, my mother! Why have you done it? Why did you think of yourself? Why could you not keep your secret? What did it matter, your personal burden, the weight on your own mind? Why did you put it on her in her weakness and age? It was for you to spare her, not to think of easing yourself. You have done an ill thing."

"I would undo it, if I could. I was shaken by the truth. I had shared her life. I felt she should share mine. I felt I owed her the truth, when I owed her silence. I had kept it for my own sake. Would that I had kept it for hers."

"Why should she have known you had broken faith? Why should I know it, Father? Why could we not keep our conception of you? Why should she lose it in her last hour? Why should I lose it in my hardest one? Why should I lose my mother and my father at one stroke?"

"I felt I was paying a debt to her, a debt that was too long unpaid. I did not see there was no repayment. And I had not thought the end so near. You cannot judge of my feeling. You could meet yours with an honest mind. I envy you, my son."

"There is no need, Father. My life has been torn away. My mother is gone; my father is changed for me; my young cousins are that no longer. It is a great adjustment. I cannot make it all at once."

"You have made a beginning," said Julius, in another tone. "And you will do it all in time. We must not give ourselves to living in this scene and fulfilling our own parts. And there is something we owe to your mother. There must be no word of the truth. There must, if possible, be no thought of it. This is the last word of it between us. You said I should have kept the secret; you were right to say it; we will both keep it now. And you need not say it was not kept from her who suffered from it. I know it was not. I shall always know it. I shall know it when you have forgotten. I shall not have your right to forget. And now there are things to be done."

"Let me do them with you," said Hester, coming forward. "Yes, I have been here all the time. I had not the chance to go. When I came in with Mrs. Hume, I saw she might need my help. And then I saw she was beyond it. And then I saw that you and your son would need it."

"Yes, we need help," said Julius. "And you know the first help we need, the certainty of your silence."

"The silence is so sure that we need not speak of it. We will not do so. It would seem to be a breach of it. But you have other need."

"Father," said Rosebery, "while you and Miss Wolsey are together, shall I go and break it to my cousins—to the children? I feel I am the one to do it. The demand on you would be great."

"I am glad to be spared. I should hardly know what to say. I hardly know how much they felt for her."

"Not what you and I did, Father. But possibly more than they knew. This is a time when truth comes to light."

"Do not ask them to simulate feeling. Your mother would not ask it. She was neither near to them nor wished to be. She was open and honest with them. Let them be the same."

"Father, do you think some unconscious suspicion influenced her, some instinctive sense of the truth?"

"No, I do not. You saw how she met it. Would you have accused me of causing her death by telling it, if you thought that?"

"You will not tell the truth to my cousins—to the children?"

"No, I shall not. It is not a thing to tell them. When they are older, it will be different. Indeed I may look to the time. And they are still your cousins. What else can they be? Do you hear nothing I say?"

"You look forward, Father. You see a future. I find it hard to do so."

"You are good to me, my son. I am happy in the child I can acknowledge. You have not spoken of your thoughts."

"Father, you have led a strange life, silent, solitary, burdened. You trod the way of transgressors, and it was hard."

"It had a meaning. It led to the future. You are right to pity your mother. She trod a treacherous way."

"Father, I have wondered if things were like this. Your affection asked to be explained. It went beyond an uncle's feeling. I used to fear the thought might strike my mother."

"It is hard not to be wise after the event," said Julius, looking into his face. "Are you sure of what you say? Are you not wondering why you did not fear it?"

"I may be confusing the thoughts I have, with those I might have had. It is a moment of confusion. Well, I will go to the children. I will try to feel to them as what they are to me."

"No, do not do so. That is the thing to forget. Be to them what you have been. You could probably be nothing more. And, as I said, do not ask too much of them. Your mother would not wish it."

"She does not wish it, Father. Those are the words I would use. And her wish is as ever mine."

Rosebery went up to the schoolroom and paused within the door. His expression changed, as though he were taken aback by what he saw. The children were seated at the table, Adrian reading and the others playing a game. They glanced at him, but as he was silent, did no more. He stood with his eyes on them, his feelings showing in his face. At length he came forward, stood with his eyes on the board, suggested a move, and waited for the game to end. It did so soon. They were not at ease under his scrutiny.

"No, do not start another game, Francis," he said, as if there had been some sign of this. "Put the board and the pieces away. I have something to say to you, that will put such things out of your thoughts."

"Is it something about Aunt Miranda?" said Adrian, looking up.

"What makes you say that? Have you noticed any change in her of late?"

"No, but Bates said the doctor told her she could not live very long."

There was a pause.

"And knowing that, you settled to games and books?" said Rosebery, as if he could not believe his words.

"What were we to do?" said Francis. "Doing nothing would help neither her nor us."

"Absorption in amusements suggests you were not in need of help."

"Those might be the right words, if we cared more for her, and she for us. As it is, we are not in your place. We cannot give up our lives to anxiety. It could not be strong enough in us. And she may be ill for a long time."

"She will not be," said Rosebery.

"Is she dead?" said Adrian.

"She is what you mean by the word. Never again will you hear her voice, catch the sound of her footfall on the stairs. The first chapter of your life is ended."

Alice and Adrian met each other's eyes, a smile threatening to appear on their lips.

"Will it make much difference?" said Adrian, as if the words fell from him.

"Perhaps it will make no difference, Adrian," said Rosebery.

"It will make a difference indeed," said Francis, rising to his feet. "We have had great generosity from her, and shall remember her with gratitude. If we did not earn her affection, the reason may have been in ourselves."

"It is spoken like a man, Francis. I am glad you have such feeling, and the will and courage to express it; and I will take you to speak for all. And if you did not win her heart, I may myself have been to blame. I may have taken too large a share of it. And I cannot find it in me to regret it. The memory will be my life."

"Is Uncle upset?" said Alice.

"If that is the word you would use, with your present command of words," said Rosebery, just smiling. "He is facing his own grief."

"Shall we all go on in the same way?" said Adrian.

"We all shall not. I shall go on in a different way, a different man. You may do as you suggest; but even you may not find everything so much the same."

"He meant on the surface," said Alice.

"Yes, on the surface you will go on in the same way," said Rosebery, in a lifeless tone, turning to the door. "How far it is the same underneath only you will know."

"Will you give Uncle our love?" said Alice.

"I will, and I am glad to take the message. I hoped to have one."

"It is a good thing words were put into your mouth," said Francis to his sister, as the door closed.

"And a better that they were put into yours. What would have happened to us without them? Enough happened as it was."

"Did you mean what you said?" said Adrian to his brother.

"I meant it in a sense. We cannot all follow your line of simple self-exposure."

"Words do not mean everything."

"So the heart knoweth its own bitterness."

"Adrian's heart has no bitterness to know," said Alice. There was some mirth, and in the midst of it Rosebery returned, laid a photograph on the table, cast his eyes over the three faces and left the room.

"What if words had been put into his mouth?" said Francis.

"He seemed to do better without them," said his sister. "Perhaps they were denied him on purpose. I think the providers of them are on his side."

"Are we supposed to be joking?" said Adrian.

"No, we are supposed to be sorrowing. We are joking."

"Do you think Rosebud is listening at the door?"

"No," said Francis; "that is a thing he would be ashamed of."

"That would in an ordinary way be true, Francis," said Rosebery, opening the door fully. "But he happened to be pausing in a natural preoccupation, and to catch what was said. And he has something to ask of you all. Will you grant it to him?"

"We do not know what it is," said Alice.

"I think I can assure you it is nothing on a large or impossible scale. You are not strangers to me."

"We will grant it, if we can," said Francis.

"Then I will ask you to give up calling me behind my back what you would not call me to my face," said Rosebery, his tone not making the best of this custom. "To do what my mother would wish, now that she can no longer enforce it."

"We will try to remember," said Alice.

"And will you crown the assurance by completing your answer now?"

"We will try to remember, Cousin Rosebery," said Alice, in a light, conscious tone, glancing at the window.

"And you, Adrian?"

"I will try to remember, Cousin Rosebery."

"Francis, you are perhaps beyond the age for receiving such suggestion. But may I take silence for consent?"

"Yes, indeed you may."

"Yes, indeed you may——" said Rosebery, bending his head and using a musical note.

"Yes, indeed you may, Cousin Rosebery," said Francis, glancing at the others and suppressing a smile.

"Then I will leave you in the assurance that this little service will be rendered to my mother and me."

There was a pause after he had gone.

"It is much to ask," said Francis. "And it is entirely for himself. He has waited until no one else benefits by it."

"Are we going to keep the promise?" said Adrian.

"We will take a middle course and call him 'Rose-bery'. That will be easier than the other, indeed the easiest of all."

"It was hard to say 'Rosebud'," said Alice. "It would comfort him to know. It was like missing out the 'Aunt' in 'Aunt Miranda'."

"Shall we let Pettigrew know we have changed?" said Adrian. "Or would it look as if we made resolves when Aunt Miranda died?"

"That is a thing that must not be," said Francis.

"And it would give him a hold on us," said Alice.

"Do we realise that she is dead?" said Adrian.

"I don't think we can. Indeed I think we must hope not."

Bates entered the room, with her lips set and a change in her eyes.

"Well, this is a sad day for us all."

Her hearers looked at her with their lips less under control.

"There are the feelings in our hearts," she said, as though conscious they did not appear elsewhere.

"Did Aunt Miranda know she was going to die?" said Adrian.

"She knew not on what day or at what hour."

"She ought to have had a foreknowledge," said Francis.

"Well, there had been signs, sir."

"Did she mind dying?" said Adrian, in an incidental tone.

Alice gave him a quick look and glanced at Francis.

"She passed in a moment, Master Adrian. And there is no need to wish it otherwise."

"You mean she was prepared?" said Alice.

"That is the implication, miss, and I do not grudge it."

"Was she surprised that she had to die like other people?" said Adrian. "Perhaps she was like Canute, and felt that in real things she was the same as they were."

"I think it is unlikely," said Francis. "She always assumed a difference."

"And dampness is hardly to be compared with death," said Alice.

"It is no moment for lightness," said Bates.

"Things are to go on in the same way," said Adrian.

"Well, that is the figure of speech, sir."

"I think the house feels different."

"From attic to cellar," said Bates, in a deep tone.

"I think Cousin Rosebery minds the most. We are to call him that, because Aunt Miranda liked it."

"There is a life that will be a blank," said Bates.

"Surely not, if we call him 'Cousin Rosebery'," said Alice.

Bates checked a smile.

"I have said it is not the moment, miss."

"I think it seems to be," said Francis. "Shock may have many kinds of outlet."

"Pleasantry is not the one," said Bates.

"Has Aunt Miranda left you anything?" said Adrian.

"Well, I have been here thirty-seven years, sir," said

Bates, with sudden formality. "And I have brooked change. But I have cast no forward glance."

"Has the thought never gone through your mind?" said Alice.

"Well, thoughts may be vagrant, miss."

"Would you rather have Aunt Miranda or what she has left you?" said Adrian.

"That is not a query to put."

"Did Aunt Miranda like you very much?"

"I had her respect, Master Adrian."

"As we had not," said Alice. "I wonder what it felt like to have it."

"I am not familiar with any other situation, miss."

A message from Julius summoned the children to a late meal downstairs.

"I expect we shall have more respect now," said Adrian.

"That is not the line of thought," said Bates.

"Shall we have to be a comfort to Uncle? It seems like a book."

"There is no need for it to be too much like one. Be natural with the master. Don't treat it as an occasion."

"It has some claim to be seen as one," said Francis.

"We shall always be at ease now," said Adrian, as Bates left them.

"I did not dare to say it," said Francis.

"Of course truth comes out of the mouth of babes," said Alice. "They are too simple to suppress it."

"Shall we have to pretend to-night?" said Adrian.

"You can observe Alice and me, and follow our example," said his brother.

There was no need for this precaution. Julius came to the table in a normal manner, and Rosebery followed in his ordinary evening clothes.

"I see your eyes are resting on me, Father. But for me there is no reason to alter my ways. My mother is present, as always, to me. To me her place is not empty. For aught I know, her eyes are on us."

"She would understand my not thinking of my clothes to-night."

"Father, I feel she understands us both."

"I am on Rosebery's level," murmured Alice. "It is Bates's fault."

"I think anything to be said to-night may be said openly," said Rosebery. "It is not a day for words that have to be veiled."

"But a day when it may be best to veil them," said Julius.

"Then surely they would be better unsaid."

"Did Pettigrew come to-night?" said Julius.

"No, I suppose he had heard," said Francis, "and thought it proper to stay away."

"And I think it was so, Francis," said Rosebery, "and that it does honour to his feelings. It is surely not natural to treat the day as a usual one."

"No one is criticising him," said Julius.

"I thought there was an element of criticism in Francis's words. There is something about the phrase, 'thought it proper', that hints at it."

"Will he come tomorrow?" said Adrian.

"There is no reason why he should not," said Julius.

"Father, I should have thought there was every

reason until after Thursday," said Rosebery, mentioning the day of the funeral.

"Then we will send him a message. It is better for the pupils to be occupied."

"Shall we prepare for him?" said Adrian.

"No, not to-night. Your thoughts will be on other things."

"And will not that hold good until after Thursday, Father?"

"It may for some time. But only to-day need be treated as an unusual one."

"No doubt you feel that would be my mother's wish."

"I am considering the matter in itself. No one can deal with the questions arising from her death."

"It seems that people ought to be able to," said Adrian.

"So it does," said Julius. "That is why we are finding them difficult."

The door was softly opened, and Hester entered the room, and came in silence to her seat.

"You have missed the soup, Miss Wolsey," said Julius.

"No, I meant to come in at this stage. You shall not have a stranger with you longer than you must."

"Miss Wolsey, surely you are no longer that," said Rosebery; "after the pleasure you gave my mother, and the added intimacy that came with it."

"I felt it was coming. And my own disappointment is the greater. But it has no place by the other feeling."

"It seems we might ask you to stay with us, Miss Wolsey," said Julius; "and manage the house and have

your eye on us all. Would you be prepared to think of
it?"

"Father, may I second the request? A home is an
unsteady bark without a woman at the helm."

"I will stay indeed and do my best for you. I see
there are things I can do. I am as interested in the
young as in the old. And I am glad not to go again
among strangers. I am not very fitted for my new
life."

"The demand on our own courage should help us to
realise that on yours," said Rosebery. "May we be as
equal to it as you are."

"It is not a very vigorous quality in me."

"Miss Wolsey, it has not failed you."

"It has threatened to at times. Often it has nearly
turned tail and fled. But I have managed to recall it."

"Then we may depend on you?" said Julius. "We
are glad to be guided by someone chosen by my wife."

"Father, I have felt it too deeply to say it," said
Rosebery, as though the sentiment should have been his.

"So you understand," said Julius to the children.
"Miss Wolsey takes your aunt's place, as far as anyone
can."

"And that is not at all," said Hester. "She takes her
own place, that of housekeeper and manager; and she
will be an adviser when she may be."

"I hope we know how to honour the attitude," said
Rosebery.

"It is really the same as Uncle said," said Adrian.

"It is exactly the same as he meant," said Hester.

"Miss Wolsey," said Rosebery, "we have to thank you

for another service, that of rendering this occasion possible to us. Without you it had been a dark hour. It
had crossed my mind that I could not face it."

"We have no choice but to go on," said Julius.

Adrian looked at him with his eyes filling with tears.

"Ah, Adrian, I could wish that my years did not preclude that form of relief," said Rosebery. "It is, after
all, the natural and time-honoured one. We are de-
barred from it by convention."

"Adrian must envy him," murmured Alice. "He has
nothing to debar him."

"Well, it had to come, and it is over," said Hester.
"We all felt inclined to do the same."

"I cannot help feeling, Father," said Rosebery, "that
it is befitting that some tears should be shed, and sym-
pathising with the one of us most entitled to shed them.
I feel my mother would look with a compassionate eye
on the weakness, if such it be."

The people actually doing this were Adrian's brother
and sister.

"We should most of us look kindly on the emotion
caused by our death."

"Father, you strike your own note. To-day is to be no
exception. You go through it as yourself. But we are
not deceived."

"I wish Rosebery did not do the same," murmured
Alice.

"Come upstairs and have your supper in the schoolroom," said Bates over Adrian's shoulder.

"Poor child!" said Hester, as he rose and disappeared.

"Miss Wolsey, I could fancy I heard a voice saying

those words of me," said Rosebery. "I cannot overcome a feeling that I have just emerged from childhood."

"Why does he think he has done so?" said Francis to his sister.

"It is a good thing Adrian is not here." .

"It was far from my thoughts," said Rosebery, not looking at anyone, "to work on the emotions or to make a bid for pity. I was simply uttering a thought to a possibly receptive ear."

"Miss Wolsey finds us indeed dependent on her," said Julius.

"I think, Father, that a tendency to be overwrought must be a feature of the occasion. We have to bear with each other."

"I think we may say that we do so."

"I have never been afraid to put my thoughts into words, if that is what you mean. I think to be ashamed of voicing our feelings has something in common with being ashamed of the feelings themselves."

"It is not the accepted view," said Francis. "It is still waters that are said to run deep."

"I was not talking of the accepted view. I was egoistic enough to be speaking of my own."

"We are not supposed to wear our hearts on our sleeves, though I see no harm in it."

"There is such a thing as not having a heart to wear."

"There can, of course, be no proof but an outward one," said Julius.

"Rosebery thinks that Francis and I are without hearts," said Alice.

"I think quite a different thing. I think, nay, I know, that your feeling for my mother was not a jot or a tittle of what mine was," said Rosebery, breathing heavily.

"Why should it have been?" said Julius.

"Father, you are right. There was no reason. If I gave much, much was given."

"Shall we have to go to the funeral?" said Francis.

"You will not have to," said Rosebery. "The question is whether your feeling will suggest it."

"Francis can come with you and me," said Julius. "Adrian is too young, and I should not take a girl."

"I think you are right that it should be a masculine prerogative. If that is the word; and in the sense of privilege it is. Miss Wolsey, may we hope to have you with us? Do your qualities put you above the feminine level in such things?"

"They will put me with the children. The feminine level is sometimes the one to be observed."

"I shall be glad for them not to be alone," said Julius.

"I had not thought of it, Father, being one of those who are now always alone."

"You identify your cousins too much with yourself."

"You are wrong. I am far from doing so."

"Your feeling would not be what it is, if everyone shared it," said Francis.

"That is true. But I might be glad not to walk in utter solitude. Not that I have done so hitherto. Even a few hours seem to have been too much for me."

"They have not been good hours," said Julius.

"Not for anyone, Father? I do not claim a monopoly of feeling."

"Only of the deepest feeling. I have my different trouble."

"Father, you have, and a more complex one than mine," said Rosebery, in a tone of recollection at once sudden and guarded. "Mine is a simple sorrow, unconfused; I had almost said, unsullied. It does not fit me to follow yours."

"We seldom meet on common ground."

"I am trying your forbearance. I am used to having an ear, and I am not of a reticent nature. As I have said, silence does not seem to me an indication of much, or a proof of anything."

"I have noticed you do not observe it."

"Father, I have tried you indeed. I think there was nothing in my words to warrant that tone. Ah, it is a strange irony. I need my mother's comfort for the loss of her. But I will make a demand on no one. I will ask for the touch of no hand, the sound of no voice. My memories must be enough."

"You are not the only person who has a grief."

"Father," said Rosebery leaning forward, "am I the only person?"

"To your own mind it is clear that you are."

"And to her who dwells with us, though veiled from our sight, what is the answer?"

"You two children may go now," said Julius, not looking at his son. "I will come and see you later. Go upstairs and be companions for each other. We have to talk of things outside your range."

"Miss Wolsey, those words do not apply to you," said Rosebery, as Hester also rose. "Your scope is surely wider."

"We will not ask her to include our family matters in it. Perhaps she will go to the schoolroom."

"There is no perhaps about it. That is where I am going. There are things there indeed that are within my range. I am not going to let them be outside it."

There was a silence between the men when they were alone.

"Father, things are going ill between us, and in this hour of all others of our lives. I find the new knowledge makes them harder for me. Hitherto, whatever I have been to you, I have been your only child. Now I am the least of your children. And I have to know I have long been that. It is a great change."

"You are what you have thought you were. There is to be no word on this between us. You must know what other men know. Everything has an ear."

"I must say the word once, Father."

"You must not. It is unsaid."

"I think I will have an hour alone; or an hour with my feeling that I am not alone; and perhaps in a sense to learn to be alone. Do not let me disturb you. I will go to my mother's room."

"You can go to the library. I am going upstairs. And when we meet again, we will meet on our usual ground."

As Julius reached the schoolroom, he heard the young voices through the door.

"Are we ungrateful people?" said Adrian.

"Yes," said his brother.

"I don't want to be ungrateful."

"Neither do we," said Alice. "We are."

"Would it be possible to be glad that someone was dead?"

"All things are possible, as you know," said Francis.

"Well, as he knows now," said Alice.

"It is possible to wish that someone was alive and a little different," said Hester.

"You will be good to Rosebery," said Julius, opening the door. "I find it hard to be so. And I cannot tell myself the reason. It may be that he took so much of his mother's feeling. The bad reason would be the true one."

"It is not in this case," said Hester, rising. "I cannot help breaking in. I already know you well enough to say it."

"I should have been a better father. We resent a person we have wronged."

"You have wronged no one. I am a judge of people, and I know it. I cannot help saying what I know."

"Other creatures stop caring for their children, when they are full-grown," said Adrian.

"I have not done that," said Julius, smiling. "I have never cared for him enough. He has a lifelong grievance. I ought to know it must lie between us. You are kind to me, Miss Wolsey. And it is kind of you to be here."

"Aunt Miranda chose Miss Wolsey," said Adrian.

"And chose her for herself," said Francis. "And that is a judgement to follow."

"We shall go on following her judgement," said

Hester. "We are a clan with our head gone. I feel I
have become a member of it."

"There is one of us sitting alone," said Julius. "I cannot do anything for him. If I go to him, I shall do him
harm. I have done it on the day of his mother's death."

The door opened and Rosebery entered with a rueful
smile.

"My resolve to be alone has failed me, Father. I
found I could not realise the companionship I knew was
there. The fault lay in my own feebleness. I felt I must
have recourse to ordinary human fellowship. I went to
the drawing-room to join Miss Wolsey, but remembered
she had sought the same relief."

"You are complete without me now," said Hester.
"I will leave you to each other."

"You will not take my appearance as the token for
your signal departure? The step might be open to
dubious interpretation. And your presence helps to
veil the fact that we are not complete."

"It cannot do enough in that way to make a difference."

"Miss Wolsey," said Rosebery, in a low, startled tone,
"you did not misinterpret me? You did not take me to
suggest that anything could compensate—could be a
substitute—take me to mean what could not be meant?
If you did, I do not wonder you felt inclined to rise and
go."

"Miss Wolsey meant what she said," said Julius.
"And you appear to mean the same."

"Can Aunt Miranda see us now?" said Adrian, with
his eyes wide.

"I hope not, if you make that grimace," said Francis. "Anyhow I hope she is not looking."

There was some mirth, during which Rosebery kept his eyes on the window.

"I think such a time as this may tend to easy emotions," he said, bringing them slowly back again. "We must take it as true that they may be one at bottom. But I do not see it as an occasion for deliberate jest."

"I meant what I said," said Francis.

"Do men ever marry someone else, when their wives die?" said Adrian.

"You must know they do," said Hester, gently. "You have heard of second marriages."

"But Uncle would not do it?"

"That is enough, Adrian," said Rosebery, with contracting brows.

But Adrian had lost his hold on himself.

"Would he be allowed to marry Miss Wolsey?"

"He would be allowed to by law," said Alice.

"That is the way to put it, Alice," said Rosebery. "We know what it is, that would not allow it. And Miss Wolsey does not misunderstand me."

"And if she had wanted to marry, she would have married before," said Adrian.

"Yes, yes, no doubt she would," said Hester, in a low, repressive tone.

"Can Aunt Miranda hear what we say?"

"I hope not, if you talk like that," said Francis. "Anyhow I hope she is not listening."

"Does she mind being dead?"

"If she can mind, she cannot be dead," said Alice.

"But does she mind not being here?"

"How can I know? It seems as if she must."

"It does, Alice," said Rosebery. "It does seem that her mind must linger on the scenes and faces of what we call her life. We have not the imagination to follow her. We are limited to our sphere."

"Is it better to be dead?" said Adrian.

"To be what we call dead? It is probably better."

"Do people really think it is? If they did, they would be glad to die."

"It is the imagination that fails," said Rosebery.

"Everything fails in me," said Francis.

"And you say it with a note of complacence. A lack of belief strikes many as a ground for such a feeling. It is a strange and pathetic thing."

"It is the freedom from credulity that strikes them in that way."

"Ah, Francis, you are not the first to think scepticism a cause for pride."

"Oh, surely I am the first."

"Francis, there is something inexpressibly jarring to me in your touch on these things."

"It is a mistake for you to discuss them," said Julius.

"I will not take refuge behind that shelter, Father. I prefer to come out into the open. As a witness I stand unashamed."

"Can we believe he is not ashamed?" murmured Alice.

"I will not ask you what you said, Alice. For you will answer, 'Nothing'. But perhaps you will tell me."

"No, not if you do not ask me."

"I think that is reasonable," said Julius.

"Well, I do not, Father," said Rosebery, his eyes dilating. "I think it is foolish and self-conscious, and I question if my mother would have allowed it to pass."

"You have no mother now."

"What a strange thing to feel you have to tell me!"

"I meant you must hold your own with the children by yourself."

"It sounds plausible, Father, or rather it serves the purpose of planting a shaft. But it avails nothing to stress their childhood. It constitutes a protection in my eyes."

"We ought to feel the same of him," murmured Francis.

Adrian happened to yawn.

"Ah, Adrian, and on this day!" said Rosebery, shaking his head and smiling. "Truly the flesh is weak." He put his hand to his own mouth.

Francis gave a laugh, and Rosebery rose and walked from the room.

"So I can never be good to him," said Julius.

"He is so good to himself," said Alice, "that he hardly needs anything more."

"I think you are good to him," said Hester, gently. "You take him seriously, and that is the first of our duties to each other."

"And you cannot do so, Miss Wolsey?"

"It is a thing for us to do together. I will help in any way I can. And now should not these little ones go to bed? Francis is included in the term to-night."

"I believe Miss Wolsey would marry Uncle," said

Adrian on the stairs, "even though we are not supposed to say so."

"No one wants to say so but you," said Francis. "And why choose this occasion for your matchmaking?"

"The day of your wife's death is an unusual one for your betrothal," said Alice. "And could there be such haste, when it would mean offering Rosebery as a step-child?"

"You can talk in your clever way, but I still think what I said."

CHAPTER VII

"Aunt Miranda is dead," said Adrian, and broke into tears.

"Yes, yes, I know, my boy," said Mr. Pettigrew. "The news came in time to prevent my coming to you yesterday. It is a sad break-up for you all."

"Things are to go on in the same way."

"But to you they cannot be the same."

"Miss Wolsey is to be here instead of Aunt Miranda."

"But to you she cannot take her place, good though her intentions will doubtless be."

"I expect she will think more about us."

Mr. Pettigrew looked a question.

"Cousin Rosebery thought you ought not to come until after the funeral."

"I should not have done so, unless I had received a

message. But I had one from your uncle, asking me to come as usual."

"He said it was better for us to be occupied."

"And I think it is," said Mr. Pettigrew, looking at his pupil. "So we will attend to his wish."

"Will Pettigrew be paid for the day he did not come?" said Adrian, in an aside.

"Come, come, the occasion is not a usual one," said Mr. Pettigrew, suggesting what he accepted as this. "You seem to have a sense of it, and you should behave accordingly."

"It is that, that makes him self-conscious," said Alice.

The tutor looked at Adrian in enlightenment.

"It doesn't," said the latter. "I don't think about myself."

"Then you are an unusual person. Not that I should rank myself amongst those most subject to the tendency."

"Will you go to Aunt Miranda's funeral?"

"I shall be occupied with my work. Otherwise I should have been happy to attend."

"Ought we to be happy at a funeral?"

"I think you do not misunderstand my use of the word."

"Francis is going with Uncle and Rosebery."

"It marks a step towards manhood for you, Francis. And I do not mean simply this observance. The change will take you all a step further in your lives."

"Will it take you one too?" said Adrian.

"I am not so intimately concerned. But it will end a relationship that I valued as happy and familiar."

"I think Aunt Miranda thought you ought to value it."

"I have just stated that I did so."

"Did she ever threaten to dismiss you?"

"I think, Adrian, that the emotions of the occasion have been too much for you."

"She was supposed to insult the people she employed."

"In the sense probably that she was obliged at times to remonstrate with her servants. It would hardly apply to other relationships. And in my professional capacity I have dealt with your uncle."

"I knew he paid for our education. Perhaps Aunt Miranda would not have given us any."

"Then he would wish you to profit by it. And you will turn your attention to doing so."

"Will you be more at ease here, now that Aunt Miranda is gone?"

"Adrian, I can only think that must be the case with yourself."

"So you suspected we were not at ease with her?"

"Miss Alice, do you think that Adrian is fit for his work to-day?"

"I expect it is the best thing for him."

"I am inclined to agree. It may do him good to concentrate."

"Ought we to be able to concentrate, when Aunt Miranda is dead?" said Adrian. "Perhaps she would rather we thought about her."

"Then we will not prevent you from doing so. We will leave you to yourself, while we employ ourselves as usual."

Time passed in this way until Julius entered, to say his first word in his new character.

"Well, Pettigrew, we are by ourselves now. We shall have to help each other. Miss Wolsey has agreed to stay and do her best for us."

"I am glad to hear it, Mr. Hume. A lady at the head of things is most desirable in a house where there are young people. I confess I should have been glad of the advice of one this morning."

"How do you find your pupils? Are they making their new beginning?"

"Francis and Miss Alice have made a good effort, one that commands admiration. Adrian does not find himself equal to emulating them." The speaker did not quite repress a smile.

Julius turned his eyes on Adrian, who sat a little apart.

"Is he doing no lessons this morning?"

"He can give you his own reason."

Adrian fidgeted and glanced about him, and at last looked in appeal at his sister.

"The reason is good, if it is the true one. And I do not wish to suggest that it is not."

"Then why do you do it?" said Alice. "You are treating him as if he were a man. When he said he must think about Aunt Miranda, it was partly out of foolishness and partly because he almost meant it. He hardly knew what was in his own mind."

"No, I did not know," said Adrian, using a sincere note.

"You seem to have been able to express it," said Julius.

"I really can't concentrate," said Adrian, sinking into tears.

"Well, you need not try to-day. Mr. Pettigrew understands."

"He does so too well," murmured Francis.

"Then he should do so better," said his sister.

Julius heard and said nothing, and Mr. Pettigrew perceived it.

"I hope I have not misjudged the boy, Mr. Hume. But I have to be on my guard against pretexts for avoiding effort. If you were in my profession, you would understand it. Not that there was any likelihood of your being so, or indeed in any other. The demands of your life are different."

"You have only partly misjudged him, which was more than he could expect."

"If he is to take no part in our work, there is nothing gained by his remaining. It is useless to him, and distracting to the others."

"I will take him with me, and relieve you of us both. I think it is Miss Wolsey's province."

Adrian accompanied his uncle with an absent expression, and presently glanced into his face. Receiving an ordinary smile, he began to run downstairs.

"Are you going to Miss Wolsey?"

"No, to Cook and Bates. Aunt Miranda said we might talk to them."

Julius smiled again, and Adrian flushed and ran on.

As the former reached the hall, Rosebery came to meet him, holding something in his hands. He looked white and shaken, and stood with his eyes on his father's face.

"Father! Let me call you that once more. I have no right to say the word. I am not your son, Father! Those are strange words to say. I shall have to face their truth. It is another breaking of my life. I said I had lost my mother and my father at one stroke. It is true in a sense I did not know."

"What is it? Put it into words," said Julius, and seemed to hear his wife saying the same thing to himself.

"Father—for that is what you have been to me—it is a strange thing I have to say. You bade me read my mother's will and discover what she wished for us. And it is as you said. Her income is yours and mine for your life, and then the capital is mine. But there is something else, Father. 'Father', I must say the word again; soon it will be forbidden to me. Father, there was a letter in the desk; it was hidden by some broken wood; I came on it by chance. She could not have known it was there. It was written to her years ago, by someone I never knew, and did not know that she knew. She is still my mother; all is not lost; some of my life is left to me. Here is the letter; the photograph was in it. Let me read it to you, that I may grasp the truth.

'My Miranda,
As you have always been wise, so you are wise now. It is time for the end between us. Anything else spells danger for you, and that is what must not be. The money is yours by deed of gift, so that nothing can arise to betray us. It must be for the boy in the end, but while you live it is yours. He

can only live and die as your husband's son. Some
wrong must be done, when wrong has once been
done. The photograph you will keep or not, as you
decide.

Yours to the end, though in silence,
Richard.' "

"Your name is Rosebery Richard," said Julius.
"Her maiden surname and this name. And that is the
thing I find to say."

"Say something else, Father. Say something to help
me. I am in need of help. Say something as man to
man, if not as father to son."

The photograph fell to the ground, and Julius re-
trieved it. It showed a large, heavy man, of a type that
accounted for Rosebery's. He seemed to catch an echo
of Rosebery in the letter's phrase.

"No wonder you have never seemed to me like my
son."

"Father, it is a hard word. You have seemed to me
like my father."

"Yes, you have done better than I. Your mother was
more right than I knew. So we lived with this between
us. We parted with it there. And I had revealed my
life to her. And she said she thanked God that she had
not dealt with me as I had with her!"

"Father, she was ill; she was dying. To her the words
were true. She was not thinking of the past. And she
had done no more wrong than you."

"She had done the same wrong. My confession must
have recalled it to her. And she turned to me and said

that! And she had done more wrong, the greater
wrong that women do. She let me accept you as my son,
pass on to you my inheritance. She lived with that on
her conscience, and died with it on it. So she had the
strength to live her own life and die her own death, as I
had not."

"Father, she was a brave woman. And I am a poor,
weak man. I must ask for your pity, as she did not
need to ask it."

"Her courage did what she needed. She put it to her
own use. She explained your unlikeness to me by citing
some forbear of her own. I questioned her command of
money, and she gave me some account of it. I wonder if
she ever spoke to me a true word."

"Father, her words were true. That is why she left
this in silence. I wish that her—that my—that the man
had done so. I wish the truth had lain covered, as so
much truth must lie."

"So that you could pass as my son, inherit the family
place, hand it on to people not of my blood. Like
mother, like son, indeed."

"Father, I need not have spoken of the letter. I
could have been silent. I could have remained your
son."

"You could not support the truth alone."

"I could not support the falsehood. That was the
burden. And my mind was in tune with yours; I
thought of the question of the place. It was the first
thing that came to my mind. And I quickly made my
resolve. I will relinquish my claim to it; I see I have no
claim. I will say I shrink from the burden of it. That

is in character and will be accepted. Francis will be your heir. That will be some compensation for you. You must have wished he could be. You have loved him as you could not love me. And it was he who had a right to your love. But I have loved you, Father. Let me always call you by that name."

"It will be best that you should. Indeed your plan will involve it. It is a sound and unselfish plan. You are an honest man, Rosebery. And why should I want to lose you? You have been a part of my life."

"Then the future is settled, Father," said Rosebery, sitting down with his face pale and full of deep relief. "We can go on in our old way. My mother's money will be enough for me. I will give my help to the house. And at your death I will go and leave it to your son. So all is straight between us and before us."

As silence fell, both men had a sense of another presence, and turned to find Hester at their side.

"So you have heard again, Miss Wolsey," said Julius.

"I could not help it. I was crossing the hall and could not pass you. I had no thought of your talking secrets here."

"You will think we talk them everywhere, that we talk of nothing else. Well, you know more about us than we knew ourselves a day ago!"

"If you will, I will know nothing."

"You will wonder what families are like, when your first emerges like this. You will not think anyone is what he is supposed to be. You can keep another secret. You see that other people must keep theirs."

"I will keep it. I feel it is mine. I feel this makes me

one of you. I feel that I follow what has happened, and that no one is to blame."

"If we accept the normal code, more than one of us has broken it. It is Rosebery who is rather sinned against than sinning."

"Father, should not Francis hear of the change in his life? I want it to be known and accepted. It somehow seems an obstacle in my path, and I long to relax and be at peace. It has been a hard hour. I may be thinking of myself, but perhaps the time has come for it. I have tried to think of others. May I bring him to learn of his future?"

"You may bring all three. It will affect them all, if you take only what is yours. There is an income apart from the place, though your mother would not have them know it. You are right that the matter is better dealt with and ended. It hinders the real silence."

As Rosebery left them, Julius spoke to himself.

"I have not lost my son as much as my wife. And I do not mean the loss by death."

"I know you do not," said Hester, in a low tone. "And I see that in a way you have lost her, perhaps in the deepest way. You must let it help you in the loss by death. We should lessen our pain in any way we can. It does no good to suffer."

"We might choose the usual suffering that comes from the usual good. It is something we have missed."

"Let the feeling pass. We should not clutch at pain. We move to the future, whether or no we will. It is not possible to be still."

"There are times when we pause and look about us."

"We think we are pausing, but we are going on. Each minute carries us forward. We find we have taken a step in spite of ourselves."

"I do not feel I have taken one."

"But you have, and you are to take another. Here are your son and the children."

"Yes, my son, Miss Wolsey, my son and my brother's children."

The latter entered and looked about them, Rosebery silently following.

"So there is something to be said," said Francis.

"Is it another solemn thing?" said his brother.

"It is a serious one," said Julius. "It will make a change in your lives. It is no good to think that money does not do that."

"Does anyone think so?" said Francis.

"I hope you do not. I should like you to value what is yours. I will tell you in a word what it will be. Rosebery is waiving his claim to the place and what it brings, in your favour. He shrinks from the responsibility they involve. He has as much from his mother as he cares to have. He does not ask much for himself."

"Then he is a rare type. I do not claim to belong to it. I am of ordinary mould. If he is sure of his mind, I welcome the news indeed. But is it not the result of his mother's death? He feels the future is empty, and does not care what becomes of it. But the mood will pass and leave him as other men. I must not build my life on an uncertainty, or on a risk of holding him to a dead resolve."

"Francis, you may build it with confidence," said

Rosebery. "You may step without hesitation into my place. I shall not be as other men, except in the sense that I must be as they are. I already see everything as yours."

"Will Francis have it all?" said Adrian.

"No, not quite," said Julius. "Only one of you can have the place, and it naturally goes to the eldest. But there will be more for you and your sister, enough to better your lives."

"Then may I tell Pettigrew that I shall not have to earn my living?"

"You may tell him there will be no absolute need for you to do so."

"Thank you," said Adrian, in a tone of gratitude. "But I suppose we must still have him?"

"You must," said Rosebery. "The need is rather more than less."

"Did Aunt Miranda want you to give things up, so that you could always think about her?"

"She did not want it. But it may be a true account."

"It cannot always be so," said Francis. "We must give it time."

"Francis, I shall be grieved and baffled, if you do not take me at my word. I did not think to have to force upon you what most men would grasp as a good. I know the term, man, is not properly applied to you, but there is a maturity in your outlook that entitles you to equal dealings. Take what is given and go forward, resolved to use it as best befits yourself and serves others. It is because you will fill the place more worthily than I, that I rejoice to yield it to you."

"But that is not my reason for taking it. And will not people think it very strange?"

"They will see it as unusual," said Julius. "We have seen ourselves that it is that. But they will adapt themselves to it. It does not touch their lives. You will find they respect you for your good fortune more than they respect Rosebery for giving it to you."

"And I think there is something in their view, Father. I too estimate the generosity involved in acceptance, and am grateful to Francis for showing it."

"It seems to me the easiest kind," said the latter. "Most people would be equal to it. Such a stroke of fortune is too good a thing."

"For the person who has it," said Julius.

"Well, Francis is that person," said Alice.

"There are things more worthy of esteem. But there is no need to blush for this one."

"We are supposed to resent people when we owe them gratitude," said Francis. "But it is not my feeling."

"Of course we like people who are good to us," said Adrian.

"I do not wish for more than that," said Rosebery, looking round in an emotional manner.

"You have paid your price for it," said Julius.

"A small one for what it is, Father. I am satisfied with the exchange. But now I find a thought occurs to me. Is poor Mr. Pettigrew awaiting his pupils upstairs?"

"Shall we have to go to him?" said Adrian.

"Yes, of course," said Julius. "You are wasting time that is not yours."

Adrian turned and ran out of the room, and Julius
followed with the others.

Rosebery seemed to debate with himself, and suddenly turned to Hester.

"Miss Wolsey, this may not seem the natural time for
what I am about to say. But the double loneliness it
brings me, urges me forward. Will you consent to share
my life and what is mine? I am conscious it is not what
might have been, even as I myself am not that; but I
feel that my suit may hardly be weakened in your eyes.
It will prevent the imputation of worldly motives that
would be such a false one. I do not rank my personal
claims high; I know the security I offer must be a factor
in the case. But I can trust you not to base your acceptance on that alone. You are not dazzled by advantages
so modest. I ask you simply if you will take what I am
and what I give."

There was a pause before Hester spoke in a low, swift
tone.

"You say it is not the natural time for you to say this.
But I feel it is the best one, if it had to be said. Your
troubles are too great for anything to count beside them.
You will not rank this one as great. I could not make a
fair return for what you gave; you would come to see it
as unfair; you may see already that you would. You
have had a great thing in your life. You could not be
content with a less."

"It is because I have had it, that I could be content. I should not expect such a thing a second
time. It would be a good beyond the lot of man. I
ask only for a mild affection and sympathy. Indeed

I could offer no more. As you say, my best is given."

"We are saying the same thing," said Hester, in a lighter manner. "Neither has enough to give, and each explains it to the other. And I see it as a loss to us both. I am the poorer for my refusal. But we cannot have what is not ours."

"I had another motive," said Rosebery, gravely. "I wished to save you from dependence, and I grieve not to be able to do so. What you could not take from a friend, you could take from a husband. It is a thing apart from my feeling for myself. That feeling I can put aside."

The door opened and Rosebery turned with a start, and in a moment gave rein to his words.

"Father, I make no attempt to disguise the truth. I stand before you a rejected man. One loneliness on another drove me to seek some help in it, and I have sought in vain. I should scorn to veil the truth."

Julius looked from one face to another.

"Well, well, my son—well, my boy, it has come and gone. Times of emotion drive us anywhere. The impulse can be taken as what it is."

"Father, there is a grain of comfort in your words. Your substitute for what you must no longer say, brings its own solace. Gladly do I answer to it, and look to do so."

"You came on a rough piece of road, and wanted to be helped over it. But you can get along it by yourself. You have left the worst behind."

"I feel I have, Father. And I feel something else. I feel that you and I are the closer for being torn apart, that our friendship may be the better for being simply what it is. It will be natural to you, and will be based on truth. It is a spar for me to cling to in the whirlpool of my life."

"You must make things easy for each other. You will be meeting day by day. But I need not doubt."

"Father, I would not take this except as the man I am. I made the offer in all honesty, and accept the refusal simply. You need have no fear."

"Miss Wolsey would wish it forgotten, and we must follow her wish."

"Anything I can do for her, will be done now and always. I take no refuge in dudgeon, bear no ill will. Nothing will be grudged to her, to whom I offered all I could. That it was not all, was not my fault."

"Yes, yes. And now you would like to leave us. You would like an hour alone. Things are too much for you, as they may well be."

Rosebery went to the door with his hand to his head and a stumbling gait, and Julius watched him until it closed.

"You have been distressed, Miss Wolsey. I wish I could have spared you. You will wonder what the next thing will be. I begin to wonder myself."

"It was only a moment, and one to be grateful for. I wish I did not feel convicted of ingratitude."

"I see how it was. He had had a hard time and little help in it. I could not give it to him. I am glad you kept your hold on yourself."

"I half wish I had lost it. It would have seemed a better thing. I should have given something on my side. He comes out better than I. He could give; I could only refuse; it is a sorry part. Do you still wish me to stay with you?"

"You will not run away as if something were wrong. Rosebery has done no harm. It seems to be his lot to suffer it."

"He will hardly take it from this. It was the result of other things. It does not stand by itself."

"It meant what it did. He speaks the truth. But it is true that he spoke the whole of it."

"He was seeking a substitute. It was much to be seen as that. And there I must say a word. I shall not see myself in that way. I shall have to do what your wife did, to be seen in her place. But to myself I shall not be in it."

"We want the place filled as far as it can be. We do not rejoice in its emptiness."

"I have not been quite honest with you," said Hester in a low, quick tone. "I mean about this other thing. There had been signs of it before; I have always met signs of it; it has been a problem in my life. I used to wonder if his mother would notice it."

"She would have seen it as what it was. She had watched him all his life. And he really kept nothing from her. He is in his way an unusual man."

"That is how it was, and how it should have been," said Hester, in a tone of accepting relief. "And it will not be long in dying. And now you will let me help you. It is you who need the help. Your son has had a distraction; I have been useful in being that. I do not think you would have sought one."

"Miss Wolsey, the children; you know what they are to me. I could not show my feeling; I had to fear to show it. And my wife thought they took my love from her son, and she was right in thinking it. It cannot trouble her now. But the custom has set, and I cannot break it. Will you give them what you can? In a way they have had a father. In a way I have done my part."

"I will. I see how they need it. They should not be dependent on each other."

"They are safe enough there. But they need something more. This house that will be their home, what memories will it have for them? They have had so little. And I would give them much."

"We will do it together. I will break the ice and you will follow. There is no end more worthy, and no two hearts more at one."

CHAPTER VIII

"I HAVE A double knowledge of you all," said Hester at the breakfast table. "Your portrait looks me in the face, as I sit here. Mrs. Hume must have felt that she lived at two different times."

"I expect she no longer saw it," said Julius. "I can hardly remember when I did so."

"I used to see her turn her eyes on it, Father," said

Rosebery, resting his own eyes on the group of his parents and himself, that Miranda had caused to be executed. "I think it served a purpose for her."

"It is a speaking likeness of all three," said Hester.

"Does that mean that the subjects might be speaking, Miss Wolsey?"

"Well, we know what they might say," said Julius. "They are not strangers to us."

"Father," said Rosebery, in a tone of deep concern, leaning forward, "would you like the portrait to be moved elsewhere? Are its suggestions disturbing to you? I would willingly attend to the matter."

"No, no, I no longer see it. And I do not hear the speech. Leave it where it is."

"There is something I have wanted to ask of you. It is my wish to bespeak a group of you and my cousins. That would have its own meaning for you, and find its place in your life. Do you give your sanction?"

"I should like a portrait of them. I will not be included myself."

"Father, I would willingly have it done as a family group. You are not considering my feelings?"

"No, I dislike living with my successive stages, as I leave them."

"It shall be done as you will, and by whom you will. And I shall feel the opportunity a privilege."

"I shall look forward to having a photograph of it," said Hester. "I think a good portrait often throws light on people. And I cannot have too much on these three interesting persons. I am always on the watch for it."

She was about to be rewarded. There was a knock at the door and Mr. Pettigrew entered.

"Am I right in assuming you have finished your breakfast, Mr. Hume? I am glad to perceive it is the case. I have sought a word with you on my way to the schoolroom, where I am due early to-day. I need hardly say it concerns my pupils; and as it does so in a somewhat intimate aspect, you may prefer to exchange the word in private."

"No, it can be said here. Miss Wolsey and my son had better hear it. It may be of help to them."

"Then I am obliged to say," said Mr. Pettigrew, his tone suggesting that his advice must appear justified, "that my pupils have lost their hold on themselves since their aunt's death. And it does not appear to be the result of the trouble. The suggestion is indeed rather of the opposite nature. There is a tendency to frivolity and indolence, and remonstrance is met by levity and veiled ridicule. The trouble began with Adrian, but has spread to the other two. I would have chosen to spare you, but knowing your concern for them, could not feel justified in doing so."

"I am grateful for the truth. It helps me to do my best for them. I am all they have by way of a father."

"And it helps me too," said Hester. "I am all they have by way of a mother, and I need the help."

Mr. Pettigrew gave her a glance and continued to Julius.

"The controlling influence has been withdrawn, and they appear to be yielding to the reaction. I have nothing to say against a youthful rebound of spirits, but as liberty degenerates into license, it calls for restraint."

"Will you send them to me and wait for them, or will you witness their discomfiture?"

"I will take the first course. I have no wish to enhance the occasion. And I have no doubt that a word in time will work in the way of the proverbial stitch."

"Dear me, I feel so unhappy," said Hester, as the speaker withdrew. "I cannot bear to see the young and helpless taken to task for being what they are. But I suppose it has to be."

"And there is a touch here of something not quite helpless," said Rosebery, gravely.

"It is simple guilt," said Julius. "They feel they can yield to their impulses, and have done so at Pettigrew's expense."

"I cannot but think that shock and disturbance have done their work," said Hester. "He should surely allow for it."

"He has done so. It is a part of his life. Complaints recoil on himself."

"He might lack imagination."

"Perception was what was needed, and that he does not lack. The faculty must be highly trained."

"Oh, I hear the footsteps. I am in such a sorry state."

"Would you like to go, Miss Wolsey?" said Rosebery, in a formal manner.

"No, I will stay at my post. I feel it is one of observation. I shall do better not to desert it."

The children entered and stood in silence, avoiding anyone's eyes.

"Do you feel you have treated Mr. Pettigrew well or badly?" said Julius.

"Badly," said Adrian, before he thought.

"Had he done any harm to you?"

"He did his duty by us," said Alice. "And that seemed to us to be harm."

"Well, there is one question answered. Did it appear to you an occasion to cast off normal restraint?"

"It was our only occasion," said Francis. "We had never had one before."

"Francis!" said Rosebery. "You do not refer to the feeling aroused in you by my mother's death?"

"It was not the only feeling. But it was there amongst others. And it was the easiest to gratify."

"So that is your use for freedom," said Julius. "You will bequeath a sense of it to other people."

"Of course we must mend our ways," said Alice.

"Then your case is settled. What do you feel, Adrian?"

"The same as Alice does."

"And you, Francis?"

"I see I have behaved like a child."

"You have behaved badly. It is not only children who do that."

"I too must mend my ways."

"Then the matter is ended. You may go and do as you say."

"Oh, it was short and sharp," said Hester. "I don't know if it was better or worse than I expected. I did

appreciate your method, Mr. Hume. No preaching and
no malice; just respectful, equal dealing. But in a way
the better method goes deeper. There were moments I
did not know how to bear."

"Father," said Rosebery, "I say nothing of the
callousness and ill will involved in the episode. But the
attitude to our loss has astonished and grieved me."

"Oh, the boy had to say something," said Hester.
"His words should not be remembered, And, if you will
forgive me, callousness and ill will were not involved."

"They will be regretted, Miss Wolsey, by one person,
if by no other."

"I could almost envy Mr. Pettigrew. He has the
chance to know and help three such appealing people.
To me late childhood stands first among the human
stages."

"I doubt if he would agree with you," said Julius.
"He has had opportunity to know it. It is the stage he
meets."

"No doubt it is different in different people. I was
thinking of our representatives of it."

"I fear they have emerged as typical."

"I fear not, Father," said Rosebery, in a sudden outbreak. "I fear they have emerged as heartless and ungrateful beyond the human level. And while I am on
the subject of my mother, which is one I see I must
learn to avoid, I must enter a protest against the cat's
being always in the room, which is a known violation of
her wish."

There was some amusement at this transition.

"I will get rid of the beast," said Rosebery, striding

towards it, with the intention to drive it before him, and the result that it reappeared at the other side of the room. "I will not countenance this infringement of my mother's rule."

Hester moved to the door and opened it, and the cat ran through it, as though it had awaited the opportunity.

"I believe in following her wishes in small things as well as in great," said Rosebery, breathing heavily as he sat down.

"The cat should not be here," said Hester. "But he has done me a service. He has reminded me of the cat at my home, and of my hope to see you both there very soon. You did not come before, Mr. Hume."

"Miss Wolsey," said Rosebery, recovering himself, "it is a pleasant prospect, and one sanctified by memory. Father, I should be glad to share with you an experience I shared with my mother. It would seem to make a bond."

"We will go by all means, when Miss Wolsey asks us."

"And, Miss Wolsey," said Rosebery, causing himself to smile, "if you would like to take our cat as a guest for yours, I will not say you nay."

"Oh, Plautus would not have it. He keeps his house and garden for himself. I don't know what would happen to an interloper, or rather I fear to know."

"I was not planning the mutual destruction of the two quadrupeds in question. I do not carry my prejudices so far."

"Of which are you talking, your prejudices or your mother's?" said Julius.

"Of both, Father. And I find the one gives me insight into the other. Not that 'prejudice' is a word I use in every connection."

"My mind's eye is on the scene in the schoolroom," said Hester. "I am glad I am not a witness of it. I hope Mr. Pettigrew is showing tact."

"I hardly think the claim should be made on him," said Rosebery.

"He should make it on himself."

Mr. Pettigrew had actually done this, as he awaited his pupils.

"Well, Francis," he said, with easy liveliness, "your Latin consists more of my emendations than of the authentic text. I should recommend another version."

The pupils took their seats in a conscious manner, showing a tendency to exchange smiles.

"We will begin with arithmetic to settle our minds," said Mr. Pettigrew, flushing at the implication. "It is not your favourite subject, Adrian."

"I shan't ever have to do accounts now," said the latter, his fears for his future being allayed.

"You will find them useful. No one should do without them."

"Uncle does not keep them."

"He may have reached the stage beyond them. I have no objection to your attaining that."

"He says they are no good, except to simple people."

"Well, the term may not be out of place in every relation. And I do not know why you have decided that accounts represent the extent of our aims."

"Pettigrew is trying to atone for his complaint," murmured Alice.

"It is true that he forgot himself," said Francis. "He is properly trembling before us."

"Who is trembling before you, Francis?" said Mr. Pettigrew easily, as though having caught the last words.

"Oh, someone we all know."

"The position of three against one may account for it. There is little meaning in that sort of encounter."

"What does he do when he has a whole class?" whispered Adrian. "It might be twenty to one."

"On the contrary," said Mr. Pettigrew, abandoning the feint of not hearing, "my classes work with me in goodwill and desire to improve. The assumption that teachers and pupils must be at variance is confined to yourselves, and you would do well to relinquish it. Otherwise I shall inform your uncle that I must confine myself to classes and discontinue private work."

"He would not know the reason," said Adrian.

"I should not leave him ignorant of it."

"Wouldn't you be ashamed of not being able to control us?"

"I see I have found a method of doing so, and one that might place the shame on the other side."

"Aunt Miranda would not like Uncle to be worried."

Mr. Pettigrew did not smile.

"It rests with you to prevent it. And your brother and sister are setting you the example."

This course was followed until the time was over. Mr. Pettigrew took his leave with neutral friendliness, and went downstairs looking harassed and spent. The question of whether or no to complain was a recurring threat to his peace. And either seemed to involve threat to his livelihood.

"We must say that Pettigrew forgot himself again," said Francis.

"Better not, until he is out of hearing," said Alice.

"Perhaps a change has come over him," said Adrian, "because Aunt Miranda is dead."

"And yet he has no sympathy with us," said Alice.

"The changes counteract each other," said Francis. "What is the good of daring to harass him, if he dares to report it?"

"Shall we always have to try like that?" said Adrian.

"We can gradually deteriorate," said his sister, "but never to the same extent."

"We shall have to live down his complaint," said Francis. "We have to meet Uncle and Rosebery; and not only have we violated human decency, but it was the form taken by our grief for Aunt Miranda."

"Well, some peoples have celebrated death with rejoicing," said Alice.

"But it is not the custom of this one."

"How much does Uncle mind Aunt Miranda's dying?" said Adrian.

"Enough to restrain himself from open observances," said his brother.

"Would Aunt Miranda mind what we have done?"

"Well, she could hardly be in sympathy with it."

"Rosebery would not have done it. It seems strange

that he should be better than we are. I am glad I am
not the eldest."

"He means we shall have his blame as well as our
own," said Alice. "It is natural to be glad of that."

"I don't think we are as bad as Francis thinks we
are," said Adrian.

"Perhaps we are sound at heart. That is said of
people who are unusually unpleasant."

"Why is it said of them?"

"Well, they are clearly sound nowhere else, and we
cannot see the heart."

"Will Uncle still like us?"

"He must have some reason of his own for doing so,
as he has no ordinary one. He likes us through everything, as parents like their children."

"It is funny to think that Rosebery is his child."

"Yes, perhaps that is why he seems to insist on it."

"Perhaps he is a changeling, and does not want it
known."

"That would explain a good deal," said Francis.

"Who is a changeling?" said Julius, at the door.

"Cousin Rosebery," said Adrian, uneasily.

"A changeling is surely a child."

"Yes, at first, but he would grow up."

"I thought he never did, but you may know more
about it."

"No doubt he does," said Francis. "He is of the age,
and he does need explanation."

"What is the subject?" said Rosebery.

"Changelings," said Julius. "Adrian is the character
chosen. I came to get some books. Will you carry these

for me, my boy? Or have you some errand of your own?"

"This can be my errand, Father. I think I was wandering about in the hope of one."

"Uncle would not let Rosebery know we said he was a changeling," said Alice.

"I wish we did not always appear to disadvantage," said Francis. "He will assume we are always ignobly occupied when we are alone."

"Then you should be alone no longer," said Hester's voice. "I have a word to say to you, and I think you have one to say to me. I believe you would like to tell me how you have felt in these last days. I am sure it would explain so much that would be best explained."

"Perhaps the less said about it, the better," said Francis. "Though I fear the line has not been followed."

"Pettigrew did not follow it," said Adrian.

"We put our freedom to a base use," said his brother.

"Now you know that is not the whole," said Hester.

"Well, it is the part that emerged."

"And by which we must stand or fall," said Alice; "that is to say, fall."

"And you feel you must keep the rest to yourselves?"

Adrian broke into tears.

"Now what did I say?" said Hester, holding out her arms to him.

He went to her, and the others looked on in silence.

"So my instinct was a true one. People do not look below the surface."

"Pettigrew found the surface enough," said Francis. "He had to have Uncle's help with it."

"I would have managed by myself," said Hester, lifting her head.

"You are seeing us after we have been conquered," said Adrian, still weeping.

"But not in fair fight."

"We conquered Pettigrew in unfair fight," said Alice. "And he followed our example."

"And it was worse, when Aunt Miranda was dead," said Adrian.

"It was because of that, that it all happened," said Hester. "Does not your uncle come up to see you at about this time?"

"Perhaps he will not come again to-day."

"I am sure he will. It is not in him to bear malice."

"How little malice there is in the world!" said Francis. "Pettigrew bore so little, that it was quite embarrassing."

"I will wait until your uncle comes," said Hester, drawing Adrian closer to her side.

CHAPTER IX

"WHAT SHALL we do about Thursday?" said Miss Burke.

"Why should we do anything?" said Emma.

"Miss Wolsey is bringing Mr. Hume and his son to luncheon."

"But she is not bringing Mrs. Hume."

"Well, I suppose not, when she is dead."

"Oh, do not speak lightly of death, dear."

"Which of us is doing that?"

"Both of us; but it is Mrs. Hume's death; and perhaps she deserved to die."

"Why more than anyone else?" said Miss Burke.

"How generous you are, when you must see a reason!"

"Do you think rejecting my services should be punished with death?"

"Yes, if I put myself in your place; and that is what I ought to do."

"Well, are they to take us as we are?"

"Well, how can we prove to them that they are doing so?"

"I think they would gather it."

"Then of course they must not do so."

"The men must have enough to eat," said Miss Burke.

"I thought they never did at a woman's table. It is the men who say so. So they ought not to expect it."

"But you do not want to be like other people."

"No, I never know how they bear it. I can only think they do not know. Indeed I have noticed they do not."

"We can have it as we did last time, but with better wine. Mr. Hume is not his son."

"You are always right," said Emma. "But won't it all be wasted on people without a woman's observation?"

"The wine would more likely be wasted on people with one. Miss Wolsey would want it to be good. You say she likes Mr. Hume."

"Surely I do not say such things."

"You mean it might be taken to mean too much?"

"I mean it does mean too much."

"She does not want to marry Mr. Hume."

"I am glad, dear. I was afraid she did."

"She surely has not said so?" said Miss Burke.

"Well, she said he would have a lonely old age. And she might want to prevent it. She might feel she ought. And indeed perhaps someone ought."

"Would you object to her marrying him?"

"Yes, I like to be the first person in her life."

"I think you always would be."

"But I like to be thought to be the first."

"Is Mr. Hume attracted by her?"

"What a primitive question, dear!"

"It seems that the son would be more suitable."

"Well, I believe it did to him," said Emma.

"Did he propose to her? And so soon after his mother's death?"

"I think he said it was because of it."

"And did she refuse him?"

"Isn't it a triumph for us, dear?"

"And then she betrayed him to you?"

"Well, we have no secrets from each other."

"Would she mind my knowing?"

"No one would want a proposal not to be known."

"We shall be afraid to look at any of them on Thursday."

"But women have so much courage. Sometimes perhaps too much."

"I wonder why he thought Miss Wolsey would accept him," said Miss Burke.

"Well, most men think that about someone, and find they are right."

"He must know he is not like other men."

"Well, most men do that too."

"And Miss Wolsey is like other women. You know what I mean."

"Yes, wanting to marry the widower in whose house you work, is very like them. What is the matter with Plautus?"

"He has been chased by another cat."

"Why did he not give chase himself?"

"Well, you know what a coward he is."

"I have no admiration for courage. There seems to be so much. And it is the thing that causes cowardice. It made Plautus run away. Well, Plautus, do you know that Hester is coming, and are you excited?"

Plautus did know, as he recognised the symptoms, but left the matter there.

"You are thinking about that other cat. Oh, look at him telling me about it. But what a disgrace to run away!"

Plautus purred his assent to what she said.

"Well, am I to have a free hand on Thursday?" said Miss Burke.

"If you need one. Mrs. Hume will not be here. Yes, I know it is because she is dead. But that makes it all the more certain."

"If we have things different from last time, the son will know we made an effort for his mother."

"But wouldn't he appreciate that?"

"You are not as simple as you pretend to be."

"Oh, no, dear. It is the form my cleverness takes."

"You mean it is the form you give it."

"Well, I thought that was clever."

"Well, make up your mind about Thursday."

"You have made it up for me. I wonder why people have such a low standard for themselves. I thought my house was run so that friends could drop in at any moment. Yes, I daresay they do not drop in. But I thought they could."

"Well, so they can. Things are good enough for that."

"It is because there are not enough friends. How you must know people's secrets! I am proud that three people are coming to luncheon, and that two of them are men. I suppose you know that, and it is really a secret. Plautus, you heard what I said, and I am beneath your notice."

Plautus's demeanour did hold the suggestion.

"Mr. Hume's son does not like cats," said Miss Burke. "I think he is afraid of them."

"That is always why people do not like animals. I do not like wolves and bears myself."

"I believe I am afraid of Plautus."

"Yes, so do I, dear."

"Shall we leave Mr. Hume and his son alone after luncheon?"

"No, they are father and son. They will not want a man's conversation. Men who live together talk like women."

"And how do women talk?"

"Like women. That is the fundamental way. Women have no reason to abandon it. Why should people talk of impersonal things when they do not have to? Men think fundamental talk beneath them, and of course it is very low. You must know about it. Or are you pretending not to have been a companion?"

"I don't think our talk is low."

"No, neither do I, dear. Well, we shall look forward to Thursday. The day will come at last."

The day came, and the guests with it, and Julius was introduced to the women.

"I think we have met before," he said to Miss Burke.

"Yes, in your house, when I came about the post as Mrs. Hume's companion."

"Miss Burke is not afraid of the truth, Father," said Rosebery. "I think there are few things of which she would be afraid."

"Applying for posts does develope the courage," said Hester. "I have only done it by letter, but the encounter had to come."

"We have only pleasant recollections of the occasion, Miss Wolsey."

"Plautus, you were to have been shut up," said Emma.

"Not on my account, Miss Greatheart. I confess to a slight antipathy to cats, but it would ill become me to have to be protected from one."

"It would indeed," said Hester, inviting Plautus to her lap, and compelling him to occupy it. "Plautus, you are so different from Tabbikin. How you are two distinct individualities!"

"I was thinking the opposite," said Julius. "Surely they have much the same ways."

"Shockingly the same," said Emma. "Suppose Plautus is an average cat!"

"Do you care for him yourself?" said Julius.

"No, Miss Burke does that now. Oh, you mean in the other sense. But Plautus does not mean it."

"He does not mind who looks after him?"

"Isn't it dreadful of him? He does not refuse to take food from any hand but ours. You will find that he does not."

"You are both very unperceptive," said Hester. "But I shall teach you better, Mr. Hume. You will learn so much cat-lore from me. And you will find it so rewarding."

"I am too old for fresh lores. And this one takes a long time, to judge from Miss Greatheart's progress."

"She is pandering to you, a thing I should scorn to do. I should not hope to win your respect in that way. I should not value it, if I did."

"Luncheon is ready," said Miss Burke. "Will you have Plautus in the dining-room?"

"Miss Burke," said Rosebery, "you will allow me to put in a plea for his presence?"

"Well, I am the only other person who dislikes him, and I do not count."

"Miss Burke," said Rosebery, in a low, startled tone, "surely that is not the case!"

"I meant I was used to putting up with him."

"Words are such an unsatisfactory medium, dear," said Emma.

"May I relieve you of the carving, Miss Greatheart?" said Rosebery. "You will talk the better to your guests. I have done it at our own table since my mother left us."

"I can undertake it in future," said Hester. "I always think it is the woman's business. It was once regarded as such. It was late that feminine helplessness came into fashion."

"There is much to be said for feminine leisure and its results," said Rosebery.

"There is more to most of us for feminine labour and the results of that. It is no good to shut our eyes to it."

"I think it is a little help," said Emma. "Otherwise we should have to face it."

"To my mind 'woman' and 'labour' are terms that should be kept apart," said Rosebery, as he exerted himself.

"There, see what a help you are finding it."

"Miss Greatheart, this occasion recalls to me the one that may be called its prototype. I feel that its pleasures are in a sense shared with my mother. It renders every enjoyment a double one."

"It is kind of you to come again and to bring your father."

"I am a sorry substitute," said Julius.

"Father! No one thought of you in that light."

"You have come home, Miss Wolsey," said Julius. "We forget that our house is not that to you."

"I forget it myself. It shows it is becoming so."

"This is a home such as I look to have myself one day," said Rosebery, looking round.

"A hope that will hardly be realised," said Emma. "Your future is not in your hands."

"Miss Greatheart, I have taken it into my hands. I have withdrawn from my position as my father's heir, in favour of his elder nephew, who has met me with great consideration. I am at liberty to sketch the outline of my future; and a home on this scale would accord with my tastes, and also with my means, as I shall experience the pleasures of contrivance. Of course it is all in the future, and I hope in the distant one. During my father's lifetime his home is naturally mine."

"Why did you act nobly?"

"I did not do so. I acted in accordance with my wishes. Prominence and responsibility are foreign to me, possibly owing to my long dependence on my mother's guidance. Indeed I have a feeling that I am still acting under it."

"I never know why self-sacrifice is noble," said Miss Burke. "Why is it better to sacrifice oneself than someone else?"

"It is no better," said Hester, "and it is not really held to be."

"It does not seem that we ought to matter ourselves as much as other people," said Emma. "But I have never met a case of self-sacrifice."

"Thank you Miss Greatheart," said Rosebery. "You do not regard my action in that light."

"It would be trying to be the object of it," said Hester.

"That would be the best thing to be," said Miss Burke. "There would be some compensation."

"Sacrifice should be anonymous, or it does not deserve the name."

"But then it would not be made," said Emma. "It would really deserve it."

"I wonder how it would feel to have a sacrifice made for one," said Miss Burke.

"Miss Burke, I fear it is an experience you have not met," said Rosebery.

"Have you met it?" said Julius.

"I remember many instances of it in my mother's dealings with me."

"They should hardly count. They would have satisfied herself."

"There is none that does count," said Emma. "Unless Mr. Hume is making one in giving up his son as his heir."

"A mild one. Francis is my father's grandson. I could not have accepted any other successor."

"I cannot help being glad that Mrs. Hume did not know of the change," said Hester. "I think it would have been a sacrifice to her."

"The question did not arise until she was dead."

"Father, may I take exception to that word? It is not one I should use."

"Well, until her death. What are we to say?"

"Such words come unreadily to my lips."

"We must use words as they are used, or stand aside from life."

"The second alternative holds no terrors for me."

"You are an ideal survivor," said Emma.

"It is what is left to me, Miss Greatheart, the thing I can be."

"You can take your part in things with other sur-vivors," said Julius.

"Father, I am not used to this dealing," said Rose-bery, on a low, incredulous note. "My mother may have been overgentle with me, but it is a harsh and sudden change. I should be allowed to make it more gradually."

"Your mother always said what was in her mind."

"Ah, there lies the difference; in the minds."

"You are not a child, Rosebery."

"It is what I have been, in a sense, Father. And we know what period is the happiest in our lives. Do not seek to belittle it for me. My claim is a helpless one, and should be met."

"It is generally the demands of the powerful that are met," said Miss Burke.

"You are not thinking of me, dear, are you?" said Emma.

"No, I should call you one of the helpless ones."

"You keep above all manner of work, Miss Great-heart?" said Julius.

"Is 'above' the word?" said Hester. "Ought we to look down on ordinary usefulness?"

"I wonder if we ought," said Emma. "Can everyone be wrong?"

"I look down on it," said Miss Burke. "I know what it is. It has nothing to do with higher things."

"Miss Burke, is not service numbered amongst those?" said Rosebery, in a soft tone.

"Not when it is enforced. I am not thinking of my present post."

"I was afraid you were, dear," said Emma. "Why weren't you, I wonder?"

"It is much to deserve that tribute, Miss Greatheart," said Rosebery. "You may be of those who do the higher things."

"I once meant to do them. I began to write a book."

"I remember you did not continue," said Hester.

"You ended by putting it on the fire?" said Rosebery, smiling.

"No, I did not. I don't think people do that. I do not know how the idea arose. I ended by putting it in a drawer. And I am not quite sure I have ended."

"I remember you tried to improve it," said Hester.

"What a memory you have!"

"It still arouses in you feelings of dissatisfaction and distaste?" said Rosebery. "You put it from you in despair?"

"No, I read it to myself in a low tone."

"I think I have heard you," said Miss Burke.

"Then the tone must be lower."

"Are you ashamed of it?" said Hester.

"Well, I don't think that is the word."

"You feel the natural self-consciousness of the artist," suggested Rosebery.

"Is that what it is?"

"So now you do nothing," said Hester, "and think that is better than the ordinary useful duties."

"Well, they are the worst things in life."

"Most of life is made up of them."

"Well, it is known to be a tragic thing."

"I have never tried to write," said Hester.

"I think that may be safely said of most of us here," said Rosebery. "Even Miss Greatheart's effort has not come to fulfilment."

"Of course it has not," said Emma. "How can effort do that? I don't see any way."

"How do you explain the thousands of books that come out every year?"

"I do not explain them. There seems to me to be no explanation."

"It suggests that writing a book is not in your line," said Hester.

"People are known never to accept suggestions, even to be rather annoyed by them."

"I also have made the attempt," said Julius. "And it likewise came to nothing."

"You put it on the fire, Father?" said Rosebery. "I can just imagine it."

"I cannot," said Emma; "I have not a strong enough imagination. He put it in a drawer. That is what is meant by coming to nothing."

"I wonder there is any drawer space left," said Miss Burke.

"That would be trying for you, Miss Burke, with your domestic requirements," said Rosebery, laughing. "Well, Father, of what nature was your uncompleted work?"

"It was a story, or part of one."

"Why did you embark on that feminine branch of literature?"

"Because of his knowledge of human nature," said Emma.

"In your case, Miss Greatheart, that was a natural reason. Our little human characteristics constitute your sphere of interest. I am far from regarding the minutiæ of our lives as unfitting material for the pen. But I should have expected some serious subject to engage my father's effort."

"There is no point in reading other people's books and reproducing them," said Julius. "I have no real knowledge of anything."

"But is there any point in adding to the amount of fiction that appears?"

"Well, it does not seem that I am going to do so."

"I wanted so much to add to it," said Emma.

"I can feel I have worked in the same sphere as Miss Greatheart," said Julius.

"We all have much in common, if unsuccessful effort is to count," said Hester.

"Miss Wolsey, I should not have thought the words applied to you," said Rosebery. "I should have judged you to have a nice perception of what was within your range."

"Oh, I just do what comes to my hand, without referring things to myself. I believe I often cease to exist in my own eyes."

"Miss Burke, that is a thing that may probably be said of you."

"No, I think I exist to myself the more, that I have not always done so to other people."

"We are in error in thinking that all the old abuses are eradicated," said Rosebery, gravely.

"They cannot be, while people have power," said

Emma. "If they did not use it for themselves, what good would it be to them?"

"It occurs to me, Father," said Rosebery, "that Miss Greatheart and Alice represent the same mental type at different stages. I could imagine them mother and daughter, if it were not a violent flight of fancy."

"I hardly think it is," said Julius.

"It is to me," said Hester, laughing. "Emma as a mother is a conception quite beyond me. And I have no doubt it is also beyond her."

"It is a conception involving all respect," said Rosebery, "though I doubt if she would value it."

"I always value respect," said Emma. "But I think I value envy more."

"Do you have much of it?" said Julius.

"No, I am afraid very little."

"I have had a certain amount," said Hester. "But I have not valued it. I have been too sorry for the people who felt it."

"Why do you value it more than respect, Miss Greatheart?" said Rosebery.

"Because people envy what is good for ourselves, and respect what we do for other people. Their sense of values is so true."

"Miss Burke, I would hazard that you can view anyone's advantages without a thought of yourself."

"Perhaps, if they are on a large scale. I find I envy people with a competence."

"I fear that that may be called the epitome of your life."

"She only means she would like a competence herself," said Hester.

"That is at the root of all envy, that we should like it ourselves," said Julius. "The next step is disliking other people to have it."

"It does seem they ought not to keep it," said Emma, "when someone else would like it. That is why we do charity; to feel that we are not keeping quite all."

"It must be an experience to live with Miss Greatheart," said Rosebery to Miss Burke.

"Yes, she is not like other people."

"May I say," said Rosebery, in a low tone, "that that is my opinion of someone else?"

"We should go to the drawing-room," said Hester. "We are beginning to talk in pairs. It is a sign that change is needed."

"It might have the opposite suggestion," said Julius.

"No, it means that general conversation is flagging and needs a stimulus."

"Why is general conversation superior to what are known as tête-à-têtes?" said Rosebery.

"Because it is a social obligation, and it is our duty to maintain it. Otherwise someone may be left out in the cold. It is not a thing that happens to me; somehow I seem to be immune from it; but it makes me more sensitive to it for other people. I might feel I was partly the cause."

"I am sure I should feel that," said Emma.

"You have a sure foothold here, Miss Burke," said Rosebery, under cover of the move. "I feel you have had much to contend with in your life. It must be a great thing for a man to release a woman from such stress. I could envy it more than the making of a worldly match."

"Who is making a match?" said Hester.

"Someone in my imagination, Miss Wolsey."

"I am glad it is not in real life," said Emma.

"Do you not approve of matrimony, Miss Greatheart?"

"Well, it puts an end to so much that I do approve of."

"Do marriages really break up friendships?" said Julius.

"You are in a position to say, Father."

"Well, I think some of mine grew weaker and died. But they might have done so anyhow."

"It is strange how all things die," said Rosebery. "Nothing escapes the common destiny. We are not the only things that are mortal."

"I thought you thought we were the only ones that were not," said Emma.

"In another sense, Miss Greatheart."

"I should get very tired of life, if it went on for ever," said Miss Burke.

"Are you not imagining an eternal routine on the pattern of your present one?" said Rosebery, gently.

"Perhaps I am."

"Then you would get tired, dear," said Emma.

Julius laughed.

"I have said it before," said Rosebery, "and I do not scruple to say it again. These subjects lend themselves too easily to a certain brand of humour. We should be on our guard."

"Would anyone like to live for ever?" said Hester.

"I should," said Emma, "if I could have a comfortable, human life and not a spiritual one."

"I think you are not serious," said Rosebery.

"Well, I meant what I said."

"Miss Greatheart, if I said anything, I should say too much."

"Well, silence is golden," said Julius.

"I do not know how it is, Father," said Rosebery, with controlled force, "but I miss my mother more on these occasions than when I am alone."

"I can explain it. You can do as you will with solitude. It does not take you on equal terms."

"There may be food for thought there, Father."

"Your son is too good for this world," said Emma to Julius. "I see what the words mean."

"That sounds quite conventional," said Hester.

"Miss Greatheart's usual object is to sound the opposite," said Rosebery. "I think the cat wants someone to open the door."

"Let me do it," said Hester. "It is such a long time since I waited on him. He goes through quite differently when I open it."

Plautus went through, as if it had opened itself, as he may have had an idea that it did, if he bided his time.

"I hope we shall soon see you at our house, Miss Greatheart," said Julius. "This is the second time we have been to yours. I should like my niece and nephews to know you."

"I have introduced them to her many times," said Hester. "She sees them through my eyes. I would not say it is through rose-coloured spectacles, but I feel it is a happy introduction."

"I want her to see them through her own, to see them as they are. That is how I like them."

"It is how anyone would like them. They are a trio after my heart. We are becoming indispensable to each other."

"Miss Wolsey, you have done much for them," said Rosebery.

"She will do more, if she will bring her friend to see them," said Julius. "It is a thing your mother suggested."

"That will sanctify the visit to us, Father."

"It will need the help," said Emma. "I am not as Hester is. I have had the chance to live for myself, and I have taken it."

"Miss Greatheart, comparisons are odious," said Rosebery.

"I do not find this one so," said Julius, smiling.

"I did the same until lately," said Hester. "There is no difference between us there."

"There is a great difference between you," said Julius, "as there is between all definite people."

"Yes, I fear I am the most definite, clear-cut person, built on the most uncompromisingly firm lines. I can make no claim to interesting vagueness. Such is my natural self, and people must accept it. And I daresay it tends to be the better thing."

"I hardly know what my natural self is," said Emma. "I should be afraid to know. Or I should be afraid for other people to. I don't really mind about myself."

"I mind about myself most of all. Myself and I are on the best of terms. We have the utmost trust in each other."

"I should be ashamed to be on such terms with my-self. We are known by the company we keep."

"You are always thinking about people's opinion."

"You are fortunate in it at the moment, Miss Great-heart," said Rosebery. "You are at any rate causing amusement."

"And amusement of the best kind, which is one of the best things," said Julius.

"There is a pretty speech," said Hester.

"And uncharacteristic of my father," said Rosebery. "Miss Greatheart is exerting a spell."

"I hope we shall soon hear a characteristic one. People's speeches are best when they are their own."

"Best of all, when they are what ought to be their own," said Emma.

"That can be said of mine," said Julius.

"Miss Greatheart is leading my father into ways foreign to him."

"I am sure of my direction," said Julius.

"We always are," said Hester, "until we find it is not ours. I never go out of my own path. I find I come on needy wayfarers there; and if I can serve them, I count it my success. A dull kind, but natural to me. A poor thing but mine own."

"Well, may we decide on a day for Miss Greatheart's visit?"

"Would it not be better to postpone it a little? It would make our time together go further."

"You can meet again as soon as you please."

"I am not used to the idea of frequent social occasions. I am still under the spell that met me when I first came to you. It is strange how one personality can determine an atmosphere. We see now that that is what it was."

"I was never in doubt of it. But it is gone, and we must go forward as we can."

"It is true, Father," said Rosebery. "I begin to see it."

"It seems to be soon for so much difference," said Hester. "I suppose the way was prepared."

"All conditions prepare the way for the next one," said Julius. "That is how progress comes."

"Or anyhow change."

"Yes, that may be the word. Well, on what day will Miss Greatheart come to us?"

"What about next Wednesday?" said Emma.

"Why that day of all others?" said Hester.

"It is Miss Burke's day out, and it is less pleasant for me here."

"Well, that is a reason, if you have no other."

"I do not need any other."

"Miss Burke, you are indeed indispensable to your friend," said Rosebery, in a low tone. "The relation precludes the use of any other term."

"We hear people talk and talk, and know we do not see into their minds," said Hester. "Their words are no key to them."

"I find them a series of delicate keys," said Emma.

"You imagine what you would feel in their place."

"No, that would be quite different."

"Better or worse?" said Julius.

"Sometimes so much better that I almost esteem my-myself. And I don't think ever any worse."

"So you are morally above the average," said Hester. "It must be a satisfying thought."

"Not very. I would rather be mentally above it. I am so glad that I am."

"No one would question it, Miss Greatheart," said Rosebery.

"We all think that of ourselves," said Hester.

"Miss Wolsey, I should not have accused you of it," said Rosebery, in a tone of surprise.

"Well, I set my face against anything that makes me look down on other people. So perhaps I have conquered the common tendency."

"What of you, Miss Burke? Do you feel you are mentally above the average? I can claim to be an exception to the rule."

"A rule is supposed only to need one exception."

"You *are* above it dear!" said Emma.

"Miss Burke has had few opportunities of showing it," said Rosebery. "Not that I intend any comparisons."

"People say that, when they have made them."

"You are too subtle for me, Miss Greatheart. I am a simple person and stand as what I am."

"We all do that," said Hester. "It is a sobering thought."

"I suppose we might improve," said Emma. "Not that I have known a case of it."

"Do you suggest there is room for improvement in us?" said Rosebery, smiling.

"You are not good at recognising cases of things," said Hester. "I suppose you have never met a case of human trouble."

"Perhaps I have not. Ought I to want to meet one? It is reasonable to want to see a thing for the first time."

"I shall never forget the first time I saw it. I have never really felt the same since."

"I suppose I must really have seen it. But I have always felt the same. Perhaps that is why I forget."

"You will lead people to believe what you say of yourself."

"Well, they would believe it easily. It is so like what might be said of them."

"I thought you were not like other people."

"So you believe what I say of myself."

"There is a convention that we must choose between silence about ourselves and self-disparagement," said Rosebery.

"Well, we could not be allowed to praise ourselves," said Miss Burke.

"Danger would lie there, it is true. Not that I should have so much to say in my own favour."

"You are beginning your self-praise," said Julius.

"I should tell the simple truth," said Hester. "What reason could there be for doing anything else?"

"Have you forgotten that self-praise is not allowed?" said Emma.

"Give us your account of yourself, Miss Greatheart," said Julius, "without regard to what is allowed."

"No, Hester is here. She would know how wrong the account was."

"This conversation does not seem to be leading anywhere," said Hester.

"It is none the worse for that," said Julius.

"Some people would not agree, for example Mrs. Hume. But we cannot go on depending on her."

"I do not see why," said Rosebery. "I am conscious of her presence. I do not know if such a feeling is common."

"It cannot be," said Emma. "Think how it would alter people's lives."

"There would be no such thing as a second marriage," said Miss Burke.

"I am amused by the way you single ladies pose as authorities on such things."

"The first wife would often understand," said Hester.

"So she would," said Emma. "There would be the trouble."

"I am in a safe position," said Rosebery. "One cannot have a second mother. No relation threatens that one."

"Some people need something more than memories," said Julius.

"I have made it clear, Father, that I have more. But I am not denying that I might have more still."

"Many people stand alone," said Hester. "They owe no debt to the past."

"Miss Wolsey, I do not envy them."

"They may not envy themselves. Some would not."

"I think their position seems easier," said Miss Burke. "Or anyhow simpler."

"The complex position may resolve itself," said

Hester. "For example, second marriages are often very happy."

"So are first ones," said Emma.

"People's experience is a help to them. They have learned to give and take. They do not expect too much."

"That seems a pity, when the chief pleasure in anything is the anticipation."

"They do not expect the impossible."

"But there must be great pleasure in anticipating that."

"Well, Miss Greatheart, we shall see you on Wednesday," said Julius. "The carriage will be at the station, and I shall be in it."

"That is a rare attention on my father's part," said Rosebery. "I think it is unprecedented."

"Oh, that is quite unjust," said Hester. "He would never fail as a host."

"Father," said Rosebery, glancing at the window, "have I your permission to include Miss Burke in the invitation? I think it would be a pleasure to us all."

"I hope indeed that she will come with Miss Greatheart."

"Thank you, I should like to come," said Miss Burke. "And it is my free day."

"I ought to wish that all your days were free," said Emma. "And I do not wish it."

"It will be in a different capacity from your last visit," said Rosebery, in his lower tone. "Then you were in a manner a suppliant; this time you will be welcomed as a guest."

"I shall be glad not to be by myself," said Emma. "I am rather ashamed of being alone in the world."

"There are reasons why a woman is better accompanied," said Rosebery.

"Oh, the world is not as rough as it was," said Hester. "I went safely by myself to your house."

"So did I," said Miss Burke. "I think companions do."

"It does not sound the right preparation for their profession," said Julius.

"They would usually be by themselves."

"It seems a contradiction in terms."

"Father, I have an unwelcome duty. I remember it fell to me before. My watch warns me of the hour, and time and tide wait for no man."

"That is such a respectful saying," said Emma. "As if they might wait for us, and we should naturally think they would."

"Well, they will not," said Hester. "Yes, Plautus, I must leave you. Do not look at me with an expression that pierces the heart."

Plautus was looking at an insect, in a manner that might have affected it in this way, and raised his paw towards it.

CHAPTER X

"I had no idea, Mr. Hume, that you were expecting guests, or I should not have timed my exit to coincide with them. I think this lady and I have met before, though I cannot place the occasion."

"You once passed her on her way to the station," said Francis. "I remember you told us of it. She was with Cousin Rosebery."

"Your memory is better than mine. I have no such definite recollection. She must excuse my claiming an acquaintance on such an inadequate ground; it was indeed no more than a semi-conscious impression."

"You asked us about it," said Adrian. "You were interested in Cousin Rosebery's being with a lady."

"I think, Adrian," said Mr. Pettigrew, laughing and glancing round, "that you impute to me the feelings that might be your own at a different stage."

"Pettigrew is ashamed of remembering Miss Burke," said Adrian.

"And you made him more so," said Francis, "as was doubtless your object."

"How does Miss Burke feel about it?" said Alice. "Is it an occasion to be so often recalled?"

Julius and Emma exchanged a smile.

"I do not check my young people," said Hester. "I take the view that they have as much right to express themselves as anyone else."

"Anyhow in their own home," said Julius.

"It is sometimes permitted there less than anywhere."

"As it used to be to us," said Adrian, and flushed as he ended.

"You need not make up for lost time," said his brother.

"Time that is mis-spent does not return," said Rosebery, hearing the words.

"That is a pity," said Alice, "as it is often so pleasantly spent."

"Come, I want you to do yourself more justice than that," said Hester.

"Does Uncle like Miss Greatheart better than Miss Wolsey?" said Adrian, as their elders left them.

"He is beginning to like her better than anyone," said his sister.

"Would a wife turn us out, because we were not his children?"

"She might tolerate us the better for that."

"It seems that we have to be tolerated. And it was beginning to be different. Does Uncle mean to give us a mother? It would only be an aunt."

"And he knows what he does by giving us that."

"I don't think he ever did know. It was a thing we could only know ourselves. If he has a wife, will he think less about us?"

"I am not sure," said Francis. "Anyone else would."

"I don't want him to have one," said Adrian, breaking into tears.

"Well, we should all prefer him to live entirely for us."

"Now what is all this?" said Bates, entering the hall. "This is meant to be a pleasant occasion."

"It is not one," said Alice. "We are foreseeing Uncle's happiness."

"Changes must come, Miss Alice."

"I believe that talk does harm. It seems to prepare the way for things. And you are always the same."

"I am what I am, miss. Father remarked on it in his taciturn way. And it always won comment."

"Uncle should emulate you," said Francis. "I don't know what your father would say to him."

"It would be a mere compression of the lips, sir."

"Will people laugh at Uncle for marrying when he is so old?" said Adrian.

"Well, it is better than crying about it," said Bates.

"I think it is worse," said Alice.

"Well, that contains a truth, miss."

"And Uncle is not married yet."

"That contains another."

"Does Aunt Miranda know about it?" said Adrian.

"If she does, many a lady has done the same."

"What would she think, if Rosebery married Miss Burke?"

"I was with the mistress for thirty-seven years, sir. And I could not say more without tears coming to my eyes." Bates turned away, as this befell her without further utterance.

Rosebery had taken Miss Burke to the library, and remained with her.

"Miss Burke, a word of yours returns to me, that you envy women with a competence. The memory emboldens me to say a word of my own, that may take you aback. I ask you to allow me to place you among them. May I feel that you understand me?"

"Not unless you are offering to provide for me."

"There is a way in which I may do that."

"Then you are making me a proposal?"

"You do understand me. We may trust a woman's instinct. May I take it as an augury of further understanding? Your selfless nature is known to me, and I am first among men to value such a nature in a woman. There could be no better foundation for married life."

"There is nothing selfless in wanting a competence, and less in marrying somebody to get one."

"You shall marry me and have one. You shall put anxiety behind. You shall be the mistress of your own home, take your stand with other wives. Other feeling will grow upon that foundation."

"I suppose you would not marry me only for my sake?"

"It would be also for my own. My mother's death left me desolate. It is another thing that I offer you, my own need. You may not rank it as the least."

"Your mother would not have me as her companion. What would she say to my being yours?"

"And a companion on another level. It was not the time for her to foresee it. But when I accompanied you to the station, on the occasion that will stand out in both our lives, it crossed my mind that marriage would be your solution, and that you were better fitted for it than might appear. I do not know what thoughts you had of me."

"I expect my thoughts were on myself."

"It is small wonder. You were treading a rough and lonely course. As I saw you pass from my sight, frail and lion-hearted, I found myself wondering if our paths would cross again. And the wonder seems to have been a premonition. You were led to a house that was to bring you back to mine. Little did you think, when you spoke of us to Miss Wolsey, that you were laying the foundation of your own future."

"It was meant to be that of hers. And I did not think very much of it. But things seem to have gone well."

"Have they gone too well?" said Rosebery, bending towards her. "I think I need not feel I am stooping to gossip. I find feminine companionship in all its aspects congenial, and may be forgiven for making the most of it. It has occurred to me that Miss Wolsey's eyes rested on my father with preference. How does it appear to the sharper feminine eye? Is it simply her concern for his widowed state?"

"It may have been that. It has grown into something more. And we must hope it will grow no further. Your father's eyes have their own object."

"I have seen it, Miss Burke. 'Miss Burke!' The name has become dear to me. I will use it yet for a while. I see how the wind lies. I see it with mingled feelings. I know not whether to feel shock or hope or sorrow."

"Miss Wolsey must see it too, and must feel one of those things, and perhaps more than one."

Rosebery tiptoed to the window, as if his footfall could be heard outside, and beckoned her towards him.

"They are coming in. And I discern an air of resolution. They are on the way to their confession. And we will hear it and make our own. We shall stand before judges who share our guilt."

"Well, my boy, you have eyes and ears, and no doubt have used them. You have seen the way the wind lies."

"Father, those have been my very words. They have actually passed my lips. And they may continue to serve us. Do you also observe the lie of the wind?"

"I do respect you, dear," said Emma at once. "Marrying a bachelor, and at a possible age! It is so dignified to be conventional. I have always thought that."

"We might have observed it," said Julius. "At any other time we should have. So this is not the only house that is to have a mistress."

"An humbler one is to have one, Father, and a mistress who will like it no less for being what it is. It will suit us both to tread the simpler way."

"It is more and more dignified," said Emma.

"Father, I read your mind; I read it as an open book. I know the question you would ask yourself. 'What would my mother say to us?' I will put it in my own way, and ask what she does say. And so well do I know her, that I can give the answer. Yes, I hear the little, cynical speech that would hold so much truth. 'Change must come, and bring other change. It is another word for life. People cannot stay at a standstill because one journey is at an end.' "

"Well, she might say that," said Julius. "You can do no more than say it for her. And it does no good to imagine her saying anything else. We can do nothing for her now."

"It seems we ought to do something," said Emma, "after what she has said."

"Miss Greatheart, we can live our lives," said Rosebery. "It is what she would ask of us."

"It seems a safe demand," said Julius, "though I doubt if she would have made it. She might have seen no need."

The door opened and a start went through the group. A change came into the room. Hester and the children entered, smiling and conscious, carrying some clothes they used for charades.

"Now we have a surprise for you," said Hester. "There is a play for you to see. Alice has written it, and Francis arranged it for us. We are the harmless, necessary actors, and you are the equally indispensable audience."

"Miss Wolsey," said Rosebery, moving forward, "we also have a play to present, a play that has its action in real life. It may interest you the more for that. You see us as we stand. It is thus that we shall take our parts on the stage of life."

Hester looked swiftly from one pair to another.

"A modern farce is it? A mating in the approved mock way? Suitable because it is the opposite. Well, it will serve its purpose. We must see one play after the other, and judge between them. I am inclined to back the children's."

"Miss Wolsey, we will see your play indeed. It will make a celebration for us on this day of our lives. But I must bring my meaning home. As we stand before you, so we shall always stand. We claim your recognition of the truth. The reality must precede the mime."

"It is you who are coupled with Miss Burke, and your father with Miss Greatheart?" said Hester, contracting her brows.

Rosebery inclined his head.

"Well, what am I to say? I am not supposed to felicitate you? It is too much of a house upon the sand. I do not know how much to take as real."

"The whole of it, as I have said."

There was a pause.

"Poor Mrs. Hume!" said Hester.

"My mother is dead," said Rosebery.

"That is what I mean. You felt she was not. And now she is."

"She would rejoice in our happiness."

"But she does not rejoice in it," said Hester, raising her eyes to his with a hint of a smile. "She no longer commands the present tense. As I said, poor Mrs. Hume!"

"You have thought of her as dead," said Julius.

"But you have not," said Hester, flashing her eyes over his face. "She had a sort of life; she had it in your minds and hearts. She has it no longer."

"This makes no difference to her. And you do not think it does."

"I do not know what to think. It makes a difference to her memory. And that I suppose is a part of her."

"It is a part of those who remember her."

"I am bewildered and uncertain. What am I to take as truth? I cannot take this. There is something unsound about it. And I do not hear Emma's voice. Why is it silent?"

"She does not venture to use it."

"And she the person of courage! But I see she must have lost it now. Courage will not stand anything. Poor Emma, how she needs a friend!"

"I hardly think she has one."

"Then be one to her, Mr. Hume, and rescue her from her plight. It is a simple and sorry one. You will not leave her in it."

"I am to be to her more than a friend. Rosebery has said the truth."

"Said the truth! Why use that scriptural phrase? It gives such a sense of unreality. But I suppose it is all unreal."

"It is as my son has said."

"Your son?" said Hester, again contracting her brows. "Oh, you call Rosebery your son. But he is to marry Miss Burke. And when people marry, there is truth between them. Or is there not, when it is truth like this?"

There was a silence.

"So you are not a friend," said Julius.

"Not a friend? You will know better than that, when you come to look back on this. Not a friend, when I am saving you from a future based on falseness, and saving you at this expense! You will come to call me one indeed."

"What future have I at my age? I can only grasp at the present."

"Stop grasping; it is not a good thing; the very word

shows it. Go back to your life in the past. It is the thing that is yours."

"Miss Wolsey," said Rosebery, moving forward, "may I remind you of your function in this house? It is not that of critic and authority. Grateful as we are to you for your service to us, we do not wish or authorise you to go beyond."

"And do I wish it? How could I wish to appear in this light, and lose any feeling I have won from you? Who in her senses would wish it? But I cannot look on and see lives laid waste for want of a word in time. I have said the word and can be silent. Whatever happens, it will have been said."

"Miss Wolsey," said Rosebery, in a more deliberate tone, "would you be taking this line, if my father had made his offer to you instead of to your friend? I am not asking if you would have accepted it; that is beside the mark; but would you have been so convinced of its unfitness? Is there not some feeling that your own life will be the poorer, that in one way or another you yourself will be dispossessed?"

"Is there?" said Hester, looking him in the eyes. "It is true that this is estranging for us, but I must see the guilt as mine. It was I who broke up our life and brought it about. And so it is for me to deal with it. I can see no question there."

"Well, Emma now follows a course of her own," said Julius. "You will have to forgive each other."

"I must sue indeed for forgiveness. To continue your scriptural phrase, I knew not what I did. But I can do my best to atone. We can go back to our life together.

It was a life that satisfied her, and that I was wrong to end. I turned aside on a way of my own. I became involved with all of you here. I am interested in the young, and these children seemed to need what I could give. But I can put it behind me. I can close this chapter of my life. It is a thing that can be forgotten."

"I shall not forget it. Emma and I will keep the memory. It has led to our knowledge of each other."

"It has not done that," said Hester, gravely. "It has done the opposite thing. It is easy to confuse them. It has led you to a misconception, and that in its turn has led you on. And Emma, the believer in freedom, the stickler for the untrammelled life! What are her real feelings? Let her speak for herself, if she dares."

"I do not dare. No one would in my place."

"I think no one would," said Julius.

"Here is someone who would dare," said Rosebery, laying his hand on Miss Burke's shoulder. "What lies between her and me is open to the world."

"And why should it not be?" said Hester. "A wish for safety and ease is a sound reason for marrying. But it is not Emma's reason."

"No, I had to have others."

"You want to lose the disgrace of spinsterhood before you die?"

"Well, we have to do everything before that."

"So your jests have been in earnest? Your gibes at yourself have been sincere? Your humour has been bitter, when I thought it was sound?"

"I do not think humour is ever sound. If it is, it is something else."

"I wonder if anything is ever sound," said Hester.

"Miss Wolsey," said Rosebery, in grave tones, "you suggest a betrayal of yourself. We might imagine a voice saying: 'Hell holds no fury like a woman scorned.'"

"I suppose that is the voice that Emma heard. And she suppressed her fury well. She kept the disguise so long, that I did not question it. And I must wish she had kept it to the end. But the moment of shock is passing. I must adapt myself to a different friend. I must be glad that her quarrel with life is healed, that the fury can die away."

"Miss Wolsey, may we say the same thing of you? It is time it was said."

"Why doesn't Miss Wolsey want Uncle to marry Miss Greatheart?" said Adrian.

"So the children are in the room," said Julius. "We have had an audience, when we were to have been one. Well, the curtain can fall now."

"Will Miss Wolsey stay here, when Miss Greatheart is Uncle's wife?"

"No, of course she will not," said Hester. "There will be no need. Miss Greatheart will manage things for you. She will be your own relation. She will be a sort of stepmother. You can think of her as that."

"They need not begin to-day," said Julius.

"Why, I think it is a good day for the beginning. They will have to realise the demands on them. And they can also realise their own claims. I used the word, 'stepmother', without thinking. It seemed to come to my lips of itself. It was a true word spoken almost in jest."

"You are not speaking in jest."

"Well, there is the meaning underneath it. As I say, the word has essential truth."

"What does she mean?" said Emma.

"Oh, what you know I mean. There are no secrets between you and Julius now. You know his life and what the children are to him. You have heard from his lips what I heard from them on the day when his wife died. I hope you will not take it as hard as she did, that anyhow it will not cause your death. But of course your bond with the family is a light and late one."

"It was a shock to her," said Julius, in a quiet tone. "But her heart would not have held out long. Emma does not know what the children are to me, but I have looked to telling her. It is true that I shall hide nothing."

"And, after all, she is only your third romance. It is not many for a man of your age. Though I rather resent your being her first one. It is a feeling for equality between you, that has no reason in it. Of course men and women are different."

"There is more difference within the sexes than between them. And perhaps men and women are different there."

"They are not," said Hester. "Look at the difference between you and your son. I have got into the way of calling him that. Miss Burke must forgive me, when she knows the truth."

"She is to know it now," said Rosebery. "Miss Burke, my mother had a story in her life, though it did not transpire until its end. My real father was not known to me, but he took thought for my welfare. We shall depend on what he left for us. And you know I have not lacked a father. And this is the time to say that you are my first romance."

"Is it the time to say it?" said Hester, idly. "I should hardly have thought it was, with me standing at her side. Not that I wish to lay claim to my priority."

"Then why do you do so?" said Julius. "It would have been easy to be silent."

"Perhaps it would not," said Miss Burke. "And she has said nothing new. She did not keep silent at the time."

"How little we know people, until we do know them!"

"I am not so sure," said Emma. "I believe we always know them. We talk of unsuspected depths, but I doubt if there are such things."

"There seem to be none left here."

"None at all," said Hester. "They are all completely open to me. And I believe it is true that they always have been."

"We can only try to feel that our own are an exception," said Emma.

"That seems an odd basis for married life."

"It may help the element of mystery," said Julius.

"You are experienced in providing that."

"Uncle," said Francis, "did you mean that you were our father?"

"I did not mean you to know it, but it is true. I also have a story in my past. It was a thing quite apart from my marriage. You yourself are old enough to understand, and you will explain it to the others."

"I have always known," said Alice. "I mean I have

known in a way. I saw there was some reason for your liking us. I guessed it was something like this, when I found out there were such things. I am glad we are your children."

"I am glad indeed," said Francis. "It is a great fulfilment. I had hoped we were."

"You will explain it to Adrian. You will put it to him as I should wish. And you will know no more until you are older; you will not seek to know. I shall remain your uncle, and you will be to me what you have been. And in our hearts we know what that is, and are glad that we know."

"What a perfect speech!" said Hester. "It is worthy of paper and print. You are indeed versed in such things. But poor children, what a burden on their youth! I wish it could have been spared them."

"Did you choose the way to ensure it?"

"I had no choice. I took the only way there was."

"Are we to tell Pettigrew?" said Adrian. "I mean about the marriages?"

"Yes, by all means," said Julius. "There is no secret there."

"We somehow feel that there is," said Hester, "or that there ought to be."

"It is because of Aunt Miranda," said Adrian. "It seems that she ought not to know."

"You must try to forget her," said Hester, gently. "That is what other people are doing."

"I don't think she is a person anyone could forget."

"Neither do I," said Emma. "I am proud that she came to my house."

"Yes, indeed," said Hester. "The woman who had been married for forty odd years to the man to whom you will be married for his last ones! It is a cause for pride."

"Miss Wolsey," said Rosebery gravely, "it is possible to conceive of pride's going before a fall."

Hester did not look at him.

"I think you will have a good stepmother," she said to the children. "I can leave you with an easy mind."

"What are you going to do?" said Adrian.

"I am going to be free, free," said Hester, clasping her hands. "A winged woman, a citizen of the world, a wanderer in far and foreign places. The thing I have longed to be."

"Will you be able to afford it?"

"No," said Hester, letting her hands fall. "It was a bright, momentary vision. You might have left it with me a little longer. But I have my plans. And the first one is to leave you. You will be safe with your stepmother."

"They will call her 'Aunt Emma'," said Julius.

"But I cannot call her that."

"You can when you speak of her to them."

"Well, I shall not be doing that much longer."

Everyone became silent.

"I think it is time for us to go," said Miss Burke.

"It must be," said Emma. "It has been time for everything else."

"Well, perhaps that is a good thing," said Hester. "It is an awkward, unbecoming occasion, better over.

MOTHER AND SON 223

Everything will soon be familiar and ordinary; and the little, humdrum problems will bring relief."

"I hope something will bring it. I was wondering if there was such a thing. We must go home, dear, and prepare ourselves for our future. It is a new demand on us, as this morning we had none."

"And nice and restful it must have been," said Hester. "The present is always the better thing. Give my love to Plautus. Tell him it is for ever his."

"Was the love for Plautus a disguise?" said Miss Burke, as she and Emma left the house.

"I hope so. In that case it can be one again. It began to seem that nothing could ever be."

"Now the children should leave us," said Hester, when the guests had gone. "They should clearly be alone. They have things to discuss, or rather to be silent about; and that must be done in solitude."

"Miss Wolsey," said Rosebery, when she had been obeyed, "my father is living his last years, and I will not have his happiness spoiled and besmirched, as it has been to-day. I may feel that you understand me?"

"No real happiness ever suffers in that way," said Hester, gravely. "That is a sign that it is not real. Your words should give you to think. There is no reason to be so careful of any real thing."

"It has been a strange scene," said Julius. "You saw us in your power, and you used it for our harm. What did you think to gain?"

"You surely did not think to lose?" said Hester, smiling. "Things that are sure in themselves do not need

such care. And how could I know you had not told
Emma the truth?"

"You must have had your reason for doing it for
me."

"Well, you said you were going to do it yourself. So
no harm was done. And you did it well. I do not think
it could have been done better. I do not know why you
hesitated."

"But you assumed I had done so."

"Oh, you want too much consideration for your own
affairs. I don't know that I assumed anything. I did
have a fear that you were marrying Emma with the
secret between you, and I shall never have any proof
that you were not. But that is all it was to me. Why
should it have been more?"

"It was more," said Rosebery, "and we are glad that
it was. It was your excuse, and it is well that you have
one. We should have sought one for you."

"That would have been kind indeed. But I think
your father, as we call him, needs excuses more. I had
better go and make them to the children."

"No," said Julius. "I will have none made. They
know the subject is forbidden. And it is best that you
should be apart from them."

"Then I had better leave the house at once. They are
my reason for being in it. I can hardly be here without
seeing them. They would not expect it, and, to be plain,
neither should I."

"You must do as you will. I will be of any help that
I can, either now or in the future. I am grateful, as I
ought to be, for what I owe to you. And anything I do

not acknowledge, I will try to repay. We need not make it a parting. There is no need or reason to do so."

Hester turned and left the room, and left a silence.

"Father," said Rosebery, "you teach me a lesson. And I see that I needed one. I must not forget my manhood."

"I wonder what the children are saying. Saying to this end to it, saying to it all."

"Would you be justified, things being as they are, in listening to them?"

"No, they are past the age. And I am also past it. I might hear what I should not have time to forget."

When the children reached the schoolroom, Adrian was the first to speak.

"Was Uncle like a man with a mistress in history?"

"Yes," said Francis; "but when it is not in history, it seems to be different."

"And the man who was Rosebery's father, was the same?"

"Yes," said Alice; "but when the mistress is Aunt Miranda, it seems more different still."

"Are we an unusual family?"

"Yes, if we have a right to the name."

"Do we have to be ashamed about it? It is not our fault."

"That means that we do," said Alice. "Otherwise it would not matter, if it was."

"I don't feel ashamed."

"Neither do any of us," said Francis. "We feel uplifted. We are superior to Rosebery, because Uncle is our father and not his."

"So that is why he gave up things to you," said Alice. "I am glad he is not as noble as we thought."

"Don't you like him to be noble?" said Adrian.

"Well, we do not want to look up to him. So it is better to have no reason."

"Did Miss Wolsey lose control of herself? I have wondered what doing that meant."

"So have I. But I shall do so no longer. And I could not dwell upon it."

"Rosebery explained it with the help of Shakespeare," said Francis. "He could hardly have managed with lesser aid."

"Ought he to have said what he did?" said Adrian. "Uncle would not have said it."

"I suppose not, considering everything."

"But he is better than Uncle in a way. He would not have had a mistress."

"We don't know what may transpire."

"Nothing else," said Alice, "or it would have transpired. It was a forcing ground for the process."

"Pettigrew would not think I knew what the word meant," said Adrian.

"Well, do not make the most of your knowledge. There are exceptions to every rule."

"He does not know anything," said Adrian, in a satisfied tone.

"Well, mind he does not learn too much," said Francis. "I have a mind to forestall you."

Adrian was on his guard against this, and lay in wait for the tutor.

"Uncle is going to marry Miss Greatheart."

"Now I must take that as a frivolous statement. And it is not a subject for levity. You forget how lately your uncle has sustained his loss."

"It is quite true."

"Then I must accept it," said Mr. Pettigrew, his tone suggesting that this put his pupil in a dilemma. "Did you offer a proper congratulation to your uncle?"

"No, he did not expect it."

"I think with some reason," said the tutor, smiling. "Francis, may I ask for your account of the matter?"

"It is as Adrian said. Uncle is engaged to Miss Greatheart."

"Then may I send a congratulation in my turn? She is a very pleasant-looking lady, if I remember."

"Is that the congratulation?" said Adrian.

"You do not misunderstand me. And I am assuming I do not misunderstand you."

"No, Miss Greatheart will be here instead of Aunt Miranda."

"We need hardly express it in that way. It is not as your uncle would see it. And what of the friend who I understood was her housekeeper? 'Miss Burke' I think was the name. Will this involve a change for her?"

"She is going to marry Cousin Rosebery."

"Now that is too much of a completion of things. You cannot expect me to accept it."

"You will come to do so," said Francis.

There was a pause.

"Am I to understand that there is actually a second engagement, that your cousin is to marry Miss Greatheart's friend?"

"She is her housekeeper," said Adrian.

"Well, I think that description may be allowed to drop," said Mr. Pettigrew, smiling. "It bears no relation to conditions as they stand. And I find a stray memory occurs to me. On the occasion when I saw your cousin escorting Miss Burke to the station, I was struck by his attentive attitude. And I should not regard myself as observant of such things. I believe I even spoke of it. It suggests that coming events cast their shadows before them."

"Do you think Uncle will like Miss Greatheart better than Aunt Miranda?" said Adrian.

"The two feelings would hardly invite comparison. And in any case it does not become anyone here to make it."

"Would you marry again, if Mrs. Pettigrew died?"

"Really, Adrian, your thoughts are running away with you. The change in your future has unsettled you, and perhaps with some reason. But if I countenance license, it must be within limits."

"Do you think Aunt Miranda knows that Uncle is going to marry again?"

"That would lead us into spheres where I am hardly authorised to take you. I do not know your uncle's views on such matters."

"If she did know, do you think she would mind?"

"It would be customary to say in such a case that she would understand."

"I daresay she would," said Alice, "and so would mind indeed."

"Perhaps Miss Greatheart always wanted to marry, and could not get anyone," said Adrian.

"I see no reason for the inference," said Mr. Pettigrew. "By the way, what are Miss Wolsey's plans?"

"She has gone to Miss Greatheart," said Alice in a casual tone. "She thought she ought not to have left her."

"There is probably nothing like living together for blinding people to each other," said Francis.

"In the case of Mrs. Pettigrew and myself time has added to our mutual understanding. But I must not adduce my own experience as typical."

"Everything adds to understanding," said Alice. "That is why people seem better when you don't really know them, and why new friendships are often best."

"Now that is an attempt to be cynical," said Mr. Pettigrew.

"And a successful one," said Francis.

"Will Miss Greatheart and Miss Burke dress like brides for their weddings?" said Adrian.

"Really, Adrian, what an odd point to engage your interest! I am not in a position to say. But it is likely that a quiet travelling dress will in both cases be held to fit the occasion."

"Did Mrs. Pettigrew wear that kind of dress?"

"I think that would have been the description of it. Her tastes have always been on the quiet side. And possibly the usefulness of the dress was a point to be considered."

"Perhaps there will be a double wedding."

"There is no reason to expect it. There is no parallel

between the marriages. Each will probably take place on its own merits."

"I don't think either has any merits," said Alice.

"Well, that is an opinion you will be wise to keep to yourself."

"Uncle has had a varied life," said Adrian.

"Oh, a second marriage is common enough," said Francis.

"But in a way it is the third. Will he have any more children? It seems that three are enough."

"It is late to give Rosebery companions," said Francis in a sharp tone.

There was a pause.

"We have wasted our time this morning," said Mr. Pettigrew, rising with his eyes rather brighter than usual. "But we may see the occasion as a reason, and we can make up for it tomorrow. I shall be here at the usual time. Goodbye to you for today."

"Pettigrew likes to know everything," said Adrian.

"And you pandered to the taste!" said Francis. "You can feel you have done all you can for him."

"Oh, I forgot! I forgot. But I did not really say it. Not that Uncle was our father and not Rosebery's."

"Have I left a book behind?" said Mr. Pettigrew, re-entering and coming to the table. "No, I am mistaken; I have it in my hand. Goodbye to you again."

"Well, Pettigrew is to be envied," said Francis. "And so is Mrs. Pettigrew. And with both of them and Bates knowing, so is everyone else."

"I daresay everyone has always known," said Alice,

"though Uncle has not thought so. He would be the last to think it. No one could speak of it to him."

"Ought we to tell Uncle that I have told Pettigrew?" said Adrian. "He might be able to do something."

"He can undo nothing," said Francis. "But I daresay he should know. He will soon be coming upstairs."

Adrian rushed out of the room and cast himself upon Julius.

"I have told Pettigrew! I did it by accident. I forgot he did not know."

"Well, what could I expect? The fault is the person's who told you. And if he profited by the mischance, I daresay he had guessed. And we are safe from him; he cannot speak of it to us."

"That is what we said," said Alice.

"Did you?" said Julius. "Children are always more influenced by an odd education than an ordinary one."

"And it is not only our education that is not ordinary," said Adrian.

CHAPTER XI

"Now, Plautus, don't pretend you do not see me. I know you better than that. You are the one person in the world who knows me as I am."

Hester spoke for her voice to reach the drawing-room, and lifting Plautus, entered with her face buried in his fur.

"I have come to say a word before I vanish. I must ask what will happen to my Plautus when his home is gone. Forth I went and provided people with chances and gave him none; and he the most deserving of them!"

"You told us what you thought of them," said Emma.

"Well, you thought better of them. Anyhow you did not let them escape you. How this is like old times and unlike them!"

Emma did not speak.

"Oh, the likeness will emerge. The storm and stress are past. I have faced the music, as the phrase goes. I have gone through fire and water and earned my release. Nothing that happens can be laid to my door. We can have an hour of peace before we part. It is Plautus who troubles me. Can you take him to the Humes' house?"

"No, I cannot. I am not going there myself."

"What do you mean?" said Hester.

"Cats do not like change. I ought to have remembered. They attach themselves to houses, and I forgot that too."

"Then will Julius Hume come to live here with you?"

"No, he will stay at home with the portraits of Miranda."

"What do you actually mean?" said Hester.

"I have never had a wish to marry. I succumbed to the flattery of being sought. And I did not like to rebuff him, in case it should alter me in his eyes. That was when I was to be the second person in his life. When I was to be the third, or I suppose the sixth, as the children are his, it was too poor a place. You served

your purpose when you betrayed him. It is not true
that wickedness never prospers. Any little wickedness
of mine has always prospered. And it is the same with
small things and great."

There was a silence.

"It was a hard moment, but a necessary one. You
had to know the truth. Julius might or might not have
told you. We shall never be sure."

"He does tend to put it off. Miranda had so little
time to know. I have a great feeling for Miranda. I
could never grudge her anything. When I knew she
would grudge me everything, I sympathised with her.
I liked her to have the first place in Julius's life. I am
disturbed now that perhaps she did not have it. But
the sixth place is very low."

There was a pause.

"How right I have been!" said Hester.

"And other things too. But I am not very troubled by
them. They are always in us; it depends if anything
brings them out; and something brought them out in
you. Will you go out into the world again, now you see
the danger of it?"

"I must, unless I am to be dependent on you."

"That would need greatness of spirit. And as I
should have the credit, the greatness would be real. But
when we have both littleness and greatness in us, ought
we to show only the one?"

"Perhaps it would be right to stay. It may be
the better and larger thing. Harm did come of the
other."

"How you are improving already! Of course the

influence of the world is known to be bad. And it is worse than I thought."

"And Plautus's future is secure with yours and mine."

"The pity is that Miss Burke's future is secure too, and that it is Rosebery who has made it so."

"What are you saying about me?" said Miss Burke.

"Did she hear what we said?" said Hester.

"No, she sounds preoccupied; and when people are that, it is always with their own affairs. I think that is really what the word means. I was wishing, dear, that I had provided for your future."

"I have to take provision where it is offered."

"I am so ashamed that I did not offer it. And I am more ashamed of the reason. We blush for our follies more than our sins. I did not think of your outliving me, when I knew how much younger you were."

"Well, people do not think of that. Survival is no part of my duty."

"But of course you will have a life after I am gone, a future that I shall not see. And it must be provided for. What a pity that Rosebery has done it!"

"You cannot suggest doing it yourself?" said Hester.

"Well, it might seem that I was doing it for my own sake. Do you think it could go without saying? I feel so many more things would happen, if they could do that."

"It can indeed," said Miss Burke. "What a change in my life! I feel the world is full of hope."

"Then did you accept Rosebery solely from base motives, dear?"

"Well, I could feel he was his father's son. I even fancied a likeness between them. When I saw him

simply as himself, my motives were base. And I suppose
they still are. But it is better to have them here. It will
mean freedom."

"No, it will not, dear. That is not all that has to go
without saying."

"Oh, I don't mind working in this house. I shall
have essential freedom. That need not mean I am not
occupied."

"Nothing essential has its real meaning. So all is
clear between us. That is one of the lowest of human
speeches."

"Will you write my letter for me? I have not had
enough education."

"You mean you have the ability and nothing meaner.
I think I have it all. Yes, I will write the letter for you,
and Rosebery will see what he has lost."

"And you will write for youself in the same way?"
said Hester.

"No, I shall write in a different way. We do not do
things in the same way for ourselves and for other people.
I shall try not to realise how I write. It might hardly do
for the last vestige of my romance."

"I think both the men will look forward again."

"And both look back," said Miss Burke. "They did
not cease from doing so. It was the main thing in Mr.
Rosebery's life."

"Did you call him 'Mr. Rosebery'?" said Hester.

"Yes, I could not say the simple name."

"Then of course you cannot marry him," said Emma.

"He called me 'Miss Burke'. He said the name had
its own sound for him."

"Take care, dear. You are going to refuse him, and for reasons that are not his fault."

"What reasons will you give?" said Hester.

"The true ones will be best," said Miss Burke. "Then the matter will be at an end. That I accepted him to have a provision, and now have one from someone else. I could even say it was Miss Greatheart."

"He will think I am bribing you," said Emma. "But it is what he was doing himself. How it will enhance your value to us both!"

"You can refuse Julius on palpable grounds," said Hester.

"No, I cannot appear to be the slave of convention. He might alter his opinion of me. I think I must just say that I have not enough to give."

"Well, I suppose that is true. So I hope he will not think I have influenced you."

"He knows you are not on his side. You did not disguise it."

"But I mean behind his back. When I was trying to put things in their true light, I did it to his face."

"Well, he may remember that," said Emma.

"Will Mr. Hume want Miss Wolsey to go back to him as his housekeeper?" said Miss Burke.

"I expect so," said Hester, idly. "But I shall not go."

"I feel guilty about Mr. Rosebery. I am afraid to think of him."

"Yes, he does make one feel like that. He has a sort of pathos. I remember I felt it myself."

"You mean when he proposed to you?"

"Yes," said Hester, just throwing up her brows.

"But it did not prevent you from refusing him?"

"Well!" said Hester, lifting her shoulders. "Now I will leave you to write your letters, and go and make my peace with Plautus."

Miss Burke looked at Emma as the door closed.

"I don't know what to think about Miss Wolsey," she said.

"You must think everything, dear. I see it cannot be helped. And I will think the one thing, that she has known the depths, and that I have seen her knowing them. It is a good thing experience is ennobling. I believe she is becoming a little ennobled."

"I think she ought to be grateful to you."

"And we dislike people when we owe them gratitude. Just as we do when we owe them anything else. It does seem they might just say nothing about it. So that is what I will do."

"I do not dislike people when I am grateful to them. I am grateful to you now."

"It is too much, dear. And when I forgot you would outlive me!"

"But I don't think we owe so much to the men we are rejecting. What they offered was easy to give."

"Then of course we must reject them. I will write your letter at once. I do feel so equal to it. See how my pen is travelling across the paper; that is the right thing to happen, I know; and it only has to travel a little further. Now you can copy the letter in your own hand."

"And I suppose the pen must begin to travel again."

"I am not sure that it ought. This is something no

person of quality would find easy. And my pen is travelling over the paper; I do not seem able to prevent it. I am actually writing the awkward words; I think it is best for them to have the awkwardness; it will not seem that I am trying to make an impression; and that is the impression I want to make. I will not read it over, in case it is not what I think. And re-reading a letter is painstaking and unworthy of me."

"Shall I take the letters to the post?" said Hester, coming in with Plautus in her arms. "It is better to let them know at once. Then the episode can sink into the past."

"The postman can take them in the morning," said Miss Burke.

"No, let Hester take them. We don't want them lingering about in the present, and preventing it from being an episode. I am sure it is salutary for us to feel it is that."

Hester took the letters in a hand she disengaged from Plautus, and went out, using them to caress him, and Emma looked after her.

"It is a pity we cannot judge by the surface, when it is so often arranged for us to judge by it."

Hester returned and sat down by the fire.

"So the old times are to come again. Indeed we might say they have come. I daresay a single life is best."

"Do you?" said Emma. "Wouldn't it have been found out, if it was?"

"You say you like living for yourself."

"Yes, but it would be very bad to think it was best."

"I shall always be glad I have known the Humes."

"I shall not. I would rather not have known them. I did not think of a household's being like that. I was brought up in a household myself, and now I don't know what to think about it. No one told me anything; but then no one told these children anything either; I mean until to-day."

"Are you ready for dinner?" said Miss Burke. "It is nearly done."

"To think that the times of our hearing that homely word might have been numbered!"

"And the times of my saying it," said Miss Burke.

"And now we feel it will all go on for ever," said Hester.

"I do not," said Emma. "I feel it will only go on until I die. I resent the people who will survive me. That may be why I did not let myself realise about Miss Burke."

"You should remember that you lived before they did, and that they might envy that."

"They might and they ought, but they do not. They envy nothing. That is their real offence. Suppose we envied nothing about them! Or suppose they believed it!"

Plautus came up to Emma and made her a characteristic gift.

"Now that is your fault, Hester. He has got into the way of giving things to me. You will have to show yourself ready to accept again."

"Ah, but, Plautus, you will not be a human being."

"What are you saying, Hester? Has your experience of the world altered you like that?"

"Well, I cannot feel I am the same."

"But you should not wreak the difference on a help-less, dumb creature."

"Oh, Plautus, what does she call you?"

"I thought that would bring you to your senses. I began to feel we had a stranger in our midst."

"He wants the door opened for him," said Miss Burke.

"It seems such a funny little duty now," said Hester.

"It has always seemed that to me."

"Well, now I get a glimpse of your point of view."

Plautus, who had had other glimpses of this, looked past Miss Burke to Hester.

"Ah, Plautus, you have not lost your trust in me. I will open it for you this once."

"Hester, I hope you will be more yourself tomorrow," said Emma.

CHAPTER XII

"FATHER, THERE is something I must say to you. I have had an experience in the last days. My mother has seemed to be near to me, nearer even than her wont, so near that I have shrunk from the thought of putting anyone between us. I have debated within myself; I have attuned my spirit to hers; I have sought from her an answer in my doubt. And I seemed to hear her voice: 'No, be faithful, my son. Be true to yourself and to me. Keep to the path we trod. We shall tread it again together.' Can I leave it to walk with another? Father, do you say that I can?"

"You have undertaken to do so. You should have made the appeal before."

"Father, I had no answer. My spirit was not fully attuned. I was distraught by earthly impulses. I was not the son she had known. Or I was the son she knew too well, and led to be his truer self."

"What harm is there in marrying and living as other men?"

"I have had more than other men. I have given more. I do not see myself turning aside to walk in the ordinary way."

"You have entered on it. You can hardly turn back now."

"Father, that trouble is not mine. The misgiving found its place in another heart. It shows it was based on truth. Another has come to a knowledge of herself, and sees her path as solitary, as I see mine lying as it has always lain."

"Oh, Miss Burke has changed her mind? And you are doing your best with it? Well, your best is good. I find I cannot do as well. I am in a similar place, and can do nothing but appear in it."

There was a pause.

"A word in this letter suggested it, Father. So our life is to be as it has been. And I shall come to a sense of peace."

"Again you do better than I. I offer no account of my feelings."

"Father," said Rosebery, bending his head and using a light, soft tone, "is not acceptance among them? Do you not acknowledge to yourself that it is there?"

"You mean I feel the ease of doing nothing, making no change, putting no demand on anyone?"

"No demand on my cousins; that is your thought. And it must bring us to another. They have heard our words. Shall we face what must be an ordeal, as they are of the age they are? The longer it is left, the more there is to do and to be undone."

"Well, let them hear us undo as much as we can."

"Has anything happened?" said Alice.

"In the sense that nothing is going to happen," said Julius. "We are all to remain as we are."

"Do you mean you are not going to be married?"

"Yes, that is what I mean."

"Have you—did they—did you all feel alike?"

"We are to say that we all did."

"Then we can be glad about it," said Adrian at once. "It will be as it was when Aunt Miranda was alive, except that she will not be here."

"Well, curb your rejoicing in the exact situation," muttered Francis.

"But she will be glad about it too."

"Yes, I think we may use the simple words," said Rosebery.

"So we can all be happy together. No one will be apart."

"Of course there is a veil between," said Rosebery, as though there might be too easy an approach.

"It must be useful to know about the other side of it," said Francis.

"Or would it be awkward?" said his sister. "It would complicate things. There would be those people to consider as well as ourselves."

"And people of a powerful nature. Only those seem to count."

"It seems it would be better to think about this side, while we are here," said Adrian.

"We do give a thought to it sometimes," said his brother.

"Do you feel it a moment for talking amongst yourselves?" said Rosebery.

"Why should it not be?" said Julius. "We have said what we had to say. There is nothing more for them to hear."

"Is there not something, Father? That the change finds us with consent in our hearts?"

"Well, it is no good to withhold our consent."

"Will you be satisfied to go on as we are now?" said Alice.

"Yes, I shall see that I am."

"Then I don't see how we can help being happy about it."

"Then in a way I shall share the happiness."

"I hope we are not the reason of the change," said Francis.

"You are the reason of other things."

"Francis," said Rosebery, "will you listen to another word?"

"Yes, a word becomes a thing of weight."

"You remember when you learned you were to succeed to my inheritance?"

"That is hardly a word I should forget."

"I have simply wondered if you had done so. There is nothing to suggest that you recall it."

"I did not know I was to be different."

"You were not. But have you not been so? Has not the loss of my mother put me in your mind at your mercy and your sister's?"

"It may have done so. But we have not acted on it."

"Then I am mistaken, and glad to be."

"And there is some reason in my being Uncle's heir."

"Francis, is that a generous speech?"

"No, or I might not have made it."

"Well, there has been little claim on your generosity," said Rosebery, smiling.

"There has been some on yours," said Julius, "and you have not been equal to it."

"Father, I should never mention in my cousins' hearing that that was not the word for them."

"That is a thing you can never say again."

"I shall not wish to. It was forced from me."

"Mr. Pettigrew!" said Bates.

"Good-morning, Mr. Hume; and may I add a general good-morning? I have a message from Mrs. Pettigrew, that she sends her sincere congratulations to you and Mr. Rosebery, and her best wishes for your future."

"Her message seems no less kind that it is not needed. We are making no change in our lives. Our venture was a late and brief one."

"Indeed, Mr. Hume, I had no idea, or I should not

have delivered the message. It hardly needs to be said. I assume the decision is sudden?"

"Yes, sudden and final. You will thank your wife and tell her."

"I will do so indeed, and she will second my hope that the change will be for the best."

"Our family will tire Mrs. Pettigrew out," murmured Alice. "And we know her health is weak."

"Would you have minded, if Mrs. Pettigrew had not married you?" said Adrian to the tutor.

"I should hardly have made my offer to her, if I had wished for that outcome," said Mr. Pettigrew, smiling at Julius. "Now I will expect you to follow me upstairs."

He went into the hall and encountered Bates, and came to a sudden pause.

"Good-morning," he said, in a pleasant tone, that seemed to lead up to something further.

"Good-morning, sir."

"So there is to be a change in the household, or rather the apprehended change is not to take place."

"No, sir. Our change is in the past."

"And I daresay it seems a sufficient share to you."

"I referred to the loss of the mistress, sir."

"You may be glad that her place is not to be filled."

"It would not be so to me, sir. There would be the void."

"I suppose you have only just heard this last piece of news."

"Just now, sir, from the master's own lips," said Bates, with truth.

"A great deal goes on beneath the surface in a family."

"Is that the case, sir?"

"There must be many things of which you do not speak."

"Well, those are as you say, sir."

"You must hear a good deal as an established member of the household."

"I have my position, sir. The family news is not withheld."

"This last piece will soon be abroad. But many things must be entrusted to your ears."

"I do not deny it, sir. I said I had my place."

"And everything is better for the daylight. It tends to grow in the dark."

"I understood it was light that contributed to growth, sir," said Bates.

Mr. Pettigrew went upstairs and awaited his pupils.

"Well, perhaps I may congratulate you all. You are to remain in the foreground of your uncle's life, if I may so express it. I hope things have developed as he wished."

"We did not ask," said Adrian. "We forgot you would want to know."

"I am glad indeed that you did not do so. It suggests you are outgrowing your childishness."

"So you do not want to be told."

"Told what, Adrian?" said Mr. Pettigrew, easily.

"How things happened with all of them."

"Well, it is outside my sphere."

"But it is not outside your sphere of interest."

"Well, gratify me in any way you can," said Mr. Pettigrew, sharpening a pencil.

"I don't think Uncle would like it."

"Then of course you must not think of it. Though your suggestions would be guesswork, and would not bear on the truth."

"I think we really know," said Alice.

"You mean you are satisfied with your guess. We are lenient towards our own creations."

"I am not satisfied with it."

"Well, it is probably erroneous," said the tutor, opening a book. "And as we are not to judge of it, we will leave the subject."

"Do you think Pettigrew will die of curiosity?" whispered Adrian.

"Well, save me from that fate," said Mr. Pettigrew, smiling and turning the leaves.

"I don't think Rosebery was troubled, even if he was surprised."

"It is unlikely that Miss Burke took the initiative in the matter. There are many reasons against it."

"And perhaps one reason for it," said Alice.

"Would Rosebery have taken it?" said Adrian. "I thought the man was not allowed to. But I expect you take more interest in Uncle and Miss Greatheart."

"It might be more within the range of my experience," said Mr. Pettigrew, glancing at a back page.

"Would you like me to tell you about it?"

"I think it is unlikely that you are able to," said Mr. Pettigrew, looking up with an open smile.

"Well, I know what I think."

"That would not throw any light on the matter," said Mr. Pettigrew with some sharpness.

"Pettigrew is his own worst enemy," murmured Francis. "He will not accept the truth, even when it is so satisfying."

"It is hard on Mrs. Pettigrew," said Alice.

"Who is taking Mrs. Pettigrew's name in vain?" said Mr. Pettigrew lightly, not raising his eyes.

"We thought she would like to know what happened," said Adrian.

"The people concerned are only known to her through my chance allusions. It is hardly to an extent to arouse her curiosity."

"So she is less curious than you are?"

"I was not aware that the quality was prominent in me. The necessity of limiting my interests to yours, when I am with you, may give you the impression."

"I suppose your interests are always those of your pupils, as you don't see anyone else."

"I have my own friends, as is natural. But it is true that their affairs are not of the same unexpected kind," said Mr. Pettigrew, goaded to this point.

"Would you have liked to marry Miss Burke yourself?"

"Really, Adrian, the question is beneath attention."

"You seemed to take an interest in her."

"When she was to become in effect a member of your family, I was disposed to do so. But that possibility has passed."

"Would you rather marry Miss Greatheart?"

"If I am to answer such a question, it is true that there might be more affinity between us."

"Do you mean that you would not marry a housekeeper?"

"Well, it is not perhaps a likely contingency."

"What was Mrs. Pettigrew before you married her?"

"She had not had occasion to seek employment. As you know, it will not be the case with your sister."

"I did not know it was the same."

"You think the tutor's family is on a pinnacle apart?" said Mr. Pettigrew, smiling and jotting something down.

Adrian was silent for a moment.

"Did you mind having to earn your living?"

"On the contrary, I realised it might develope gifts that would otherwise lie dormant."

"What are the gifts?"

"Patience, perhaps, and tolerance of idle curiosity."

"I don't call those gifts."

"It does not do to underrate them."

"Then why does everyone do it?" said Alice.

"Oh, you are all in the stage when you think that genius and fame are the normal human lot. You will have to learn your mistake."

"As Pettigrew did, when he realised his gifts," murmured Francis.

"I did not give you a list of them, in case patience was not amongst yours," said Mr. Pettigrew, in a complex tone.

"I hope it is among Mrs. Pettigrew's, if she hears of the fortunes of our family."

"I think, Francis, that that is a subject upon which you might learn to be silent."

"I hope Pettigrew will follow his own suggestion," said Francis, when the tutor had left them.

"I expect he has told everyone about Uncle and us," said Adrian.

"Well, you set him the example and gave him the opportunity. You have no right to complain."

"It is strange that Aunt Miranda did not know, until just before she died. It seems it was almost a pity to tell her then."

"That might often be said of eleventh-hour confessions."

"And said truly of them," said Alice. "They are seldom of a pleasant kind, and it is hardly the time for unpleasantness."

"Perhaps they hasten people's death," said Adrian.

"That is really not their usual object," said Francis.

"This seems to have hastened Aunt Miranda's."

"You mean there are exceptions to every rule?"

"They are meant to do the opposite," said Alice, "and make the most of the last moments. And in books they do make them go a long way."

"It is strange that someone might have been in Aunt Miranda's place," said Adrian.

"It never seemed real," said his sister. "I wonder how it seemed to them. Perhaps Uncle had had enough of reality and wanted something different. And perhaps he would have had it, if it had not been for us."

"Aunt Miranda would be glad of our existence at last," said Francis.

"I would rather Uncle was glad of it," said Adrian. "It is a pity they can't be glad of it together."

The door opened and Rosebery entered, and came smilingly forward.

"Now in a sense we enter on a new chapter. The time of our uncertainty is past. I am at a stage between you and your uncle, and must do my best in it. Shall we try a game together? I have noticed that games play a part in your life."

The occasion of which this was true, came into their minds.

"It is the others who play games," said Adrian. "I would rather read."

"It will do you no harm to take your part in one with them."

"Our games are for two people. We haven't any other kind."

"You must have some cards. There is a game for four with those, that you should learn. I suppose you know how to deal."

They did not, but Francis and Alice soon did, and Adrian's incapacity was accepted.

"A game is like a lesson," he said.

"While you are learning it," said Rosebery. "It will not always be."

"Is there anything wrong in not playing games?"

"It is unsocial to sit apart, and that is not a pleasant quality."

"Games for four will not be any good to us," said Adrian, realising his words too late.

Rosebery simply smiled.

"One person can take the place of two. I will explain that to you presently."

He was as good as his word, and Adrian was confirmed in his view of games. When this one ended, the others were striving with mirth, and he with another emotion.

"Will Rosebery do things for us now, instead of for Aunt Miranda?" he whispered.

"What should we have thought of her death," said Francis, "if we had known we were to take her place?"

"And what would she have thought?" said Alice.

"We will have many more games together," said Rosebery, putting up the cards with this in view.

As he spoke, the door opened, and he saw the children's faces light.

"Father," he said, rising, "I have tried and I have failed. I have done my best, and it is not enough. I have striven to the end of my strength, and it does not avail. I have no place in this house, on the scene of my mother's life and mine. So now there is something to be told. Do not fear; it is no great thing. I had a letter when my mother died; I did not tell you of it; you were having enough of me and my troubles, of another man and his sorry fate. The letter must have come from my father. It was a simple word, signed: 'an old man whose thought must be on you'. I must go to him, Father. I care not who he is, what he is; he is the man who with my mother gave me life. And when he dies, I will order my own days. I will not fail you and return; I will not fail your children. They are with their father, as I shall be with mine. But this is no last farewell. We shall always meet. For your sake, for mine, for my mother's, that must be. But for the moment it is a parting, if only of the ways. Father, goodbye; that is what you have been to me; we will not say something was wanting, though we know what we do."

Rosebery gave his hand to Julius, and went to the door without looking at the children, as though he recognised he was nothing to them. Adrian spoke before he reached it.

"Shan't we ever see you again?"

"You did not listen?" said Rosebery, gently. "You did not hear? You will see me when I come to the house. You will be about it, as usual, more than you are now. You see I shall be gone. I shall realise that, when I return; that I am gone."

Adrian broke into weeping.

"Ah, Adrian, we know your tears, and know they are soon dried."

"Most tears are," said Julius. "But some of us do not win them."

"I want none, Father. Let me leave smiles behind. I know they smile at heart."

"You know too much," said Francis. "And we do not know enough. Why cannot you visit your father and return?"

"Return where?"

"Here, where you have spent your life."

"Yes, it is late to begin again," said Rosebery, in a quiet tone.

"What do you feel about his going?" said Alice to Francis.

"I believe I feel grief."

"And I feel alarm. The family will be too small. We shall not be enough for Uncle."

"Does Uncle love Rosebery?" said Adrian.

"Yes, in a way. He was his father for too long. He will never lose all the feeling."

"And absence will make his heart grow fond," said Francis. "The thought of it makes mine do so."

"I believe my heart was always fond," said Alice.

"Have you your father's letter?" said Julius to Rosebery.

Rosebery handed it to him.

"There is no address. I thought there might be none. After all these years there would hardly be one."

"Let me see the letter, Father."

"You knew it; you must have known. How could you make your plans, if you did not know your destination?"

"I had made no plans. There was need of none. I was going to the writer of the letter, wherever it might be. And I will go. Something will guide my steps."

"What can do that?" said Alice.

"Nothing you would know, no voice that you would hear."

"Well, listen to the voice," said Julius, "and tell me where to send your letters and anything else you will need."

Rosebery sat down and covered his face with his hands.

"Father, you will not believe me. But I did not think of the address. It mattered nothing to me where it was, what it was; I was simply going to it. Until I set

forth, I had no need to know it. But how can you believe such a word?"

"I believe it, my boy. No one else would do so. I
wonder at myself, but I find it true. You did not think
of going, until you felt urged to make a scene. And then
the thought did its own work."

"I meant to go, Father."

"You would have gone and returned. Though perhaps not before your father's death."

"He can't go now," said Adrian to Alice.

"No, he must stay here. It is the only address he
knows."

"Are you glad he is not going?"

"Hardly as glad as I thought I should be."

"I think that shows you are glad."

"Well, our life will be easier with him. We recognise
what he does for it."

"Haven't we done him justice?"

"No, we have only just begun to do it. And no one
could ever do him enough."

"I have never known anyone who needed so much,"
said Francis.

"I think he likes it as well as needs it," said Adrian.

There was a silence.

"Father, will you join us in a game of cards?" said
Rosebery, drawing out a chair. "We only need four
players, but Adrian will make no demur to being left
out."

"Will nothing else absorb Rosebery's energy?" murmured Francis. "If only Aunt Miranda were alive!"

"Francis, that will be the epitome of my life."

"Would she have liked us to play cards?" said Adrian.

"Was it that doubt, that prevented your playing?" said Rosebery, with a smile. "I can relieve you of it. She taught me to play herself, when I was a boy."

"And now has left him partnerless," murmured Francis.

"And now has left me as you say, Francis," said Rosebery.

THE END

Date Due